BUILDING SIGHT VOCABULARY: GR...
TABLE OF CONTENT...

BUILDING SIGHT VOCABULARY: GRADE 1 - BOOK 3

INTRODUCTION

Sight words are those words which occur most frequently in the English language and often have no content to help the student remember them. Words like *this* and *has* are more difficult to remember than *boat* or *clown* because sight words are not easily linked to a mental picture. A beginning vocabulary is made up almost entirely of sight words.

A large sight vocabulary helps the student read faster. Students who read more quickly feel confident in their skill and will be more likely to read for fun, thus ensuring greater practice time. Comprehension is also expanded through the use of sight words. Readers spend less time decoding words and more time focusing on the sentence meaning. Moreover, sight words often provide context clues to further develop important process skills.

ORGANIZATION

Building Sight Word Vocabulary, Grade 1–Book 3 focuses on the theme of careers. The characters from Books 1 and 2 are introduced once again. Each lesson, with the exception of Lesson 1, introduces four or five sight words. (Lesson 1 introduces number words.) A lesson is comprised of two Practice pages and a story. A game and a one-page review are also included at the end of each unit.

Practice Pages: The first Practice page introduces the sight words in Key Sentences. A variety of activities provides practice and reinforces word recognition. Activities include matching, writing sentences, adding suffixes, and cloze procedure. The second Practice page reviews the words just taught and those learned in the previous lesson. Activities on this page might include forming contractions and compound words, word finds, and sentence context.

Stories: Each story is designed to be copied on a single sheet of paper. To make the book, students first fold the page in half top to bottom, then from left to right. The stories are written so that students practice the new sight words in context, as well as review previously taught words. Unfamiliar words are underlined in the story and identified by labels in art.

Games: A game accompanies each unit to review the sight words in a fun context. They are to be mounted on construction paper and cut out. Game pieces can be stored in envelopes for easy management.

Reviews: The last page of each unit reviews words in sentence context. Student recognition and comprehension of the words can be checked at this time.

USE

Determine the implementation that best fits your students' needs. The following plan suggests a format you may wish to use:

On the first day, write the Key Sentence(s) on the board and underline Key Words. Read the sentence(s) several times, pointing to each word. Then have students read the sentence(s) as you point to each word. Give students the first Practice page to complete after providing directions. On the second day, review the Key Sentence(s) and Key Words. Students then complete the second Practice page. On the third day, students prepare the booklets. After reviewing the Key Sentence(s), choral read the story several times. Continue to allow students to practice rereading the story in a variety of settings: in small groups, in pairs, or individually into a tape recorder.

ADDITIONAL FEATURES

Assessment An Assessment test is found on pages 4 and 5. You can use the test as a diagnostic tool by administering it before students begin the activities. After they have completed all the lessons, let them retake it to gauge their progress.

Parent Letter Send the Parent Letter home with students.

Word List

Building Sight Vocabulary 3, SV 6212-1

Name_____   Date _____

1. ● every ○ eat ○ very	2. ○ laugh ○ place ○ play	3. ○ goes ○ good ○ got	4. ○ over ○ on ○ own
5. ○ took ○ thought ○ thing	6. ○ build ○ but ○ live	7. ○ place ○ put ○ part	8. ○ ever ○ each ○ eat
9. ○ while ○ with ○ which	10. ○ other ○ their ○ over	11. ○ than ○ that ○ three	12. ○ now ○ small ○ more
13. ○ next ○ not ○ never	14. ○ saw ○ sure ○ soon	15. ○ cold ○ kind ○ know	16. ○ she ○ could ○ should
17. ○ pick ○ pull ○ keep	18. ○ start ○ shall ○ than	19. ○ got ○ grow ○ get	20. ○ eat ○ eight ○ enough
21. ○ sit ○ some ○ set	22. ○ small ○ many ○ say	23. ○ can ○ carry ○ call	24. ○ come ○ cold ○ carry

Assessment:
Refer to the Answer Key on page 95 to see which words students mark for this Assessment.

Name _____   Date _____

1. ○ after ○ along ○ also	2. ○ few ○ fine ○ fly	3. ○ last ○ lost ○ ate	4. ○ number ○ myself ○ other
5. ○ other ○ part ○ old	6. ○ clean ○ cost ○ cold	7. ○ need ○ keep ○ kind	8. ○ before ○ better ○ bring
9. ○ grow ○ gave ○ goes	10. ○ more ○ made ○ most	11. ○ another ○ along ○ also	12. ○ part ○ please ○ place
13. ○ sleep ○ seven ○ stay	14. ○ hold ○ high ○ help	15. ○ than ○ through ○ thought	16. ○ can ○ cold ○ cost
17. ○ saw ○ sit ○ six	18. ○ yes ○ say ○ you	19. ○ place ○ play ○ please	20. ○ other ○ together ○ thought
21. ○ over ○ enough ○ end	22. ○ where ○ which ○ when	23. ○ warm ○ work ○ would	24. ○ because ○ buy ○ build

Assessment:
Refer to the Answer Key on page 95 to see which words students mark for this Assessment.

Dear Parent,

Becoming a good reader is a challenge during the primary education years. Children discover how sounds and words form sentences and paragraphs. Building and retaining a strong sight vocabulary is essential to the reading process. *Sight words* are those words which occur most frequently in the English language and often have no content to help the reader remember them. Recognizing these basic words helps the child read faster and develop strong decoding skills, thus making a better reader.

During the year, your child will be developing sight vocabulary through practice sheets, booklets, and games. After being introduced to four or five core words, your child will bring home the completed practice sheets and a four-page booklet. Games will also be included at the end of each unit. Your child will progress at a much faster rate if you will consistently review and practice what is brought home. To best help your child, please consider the following suggestions:

- Listen to your child read the new stories several times. Ask questions to help your child understand the meaning of the story.
- Save all the stories. Encourage your child to frequently reread the old stories.
- Together, review practice pages. Have your child read the Key Sentences and Key Words. Then find ways to use those sentences and words frequently.
- Play the new games and practice the new words with your child. Continue to play the old games for review.

Thank you for your help. Your child and I appreciate your assistance and reinforcement in this learning process.

Cordially,

Name _____   Date _____

Dan	Mandy	Eric	Jenny

Kim	Nat	Tony	Rose

Lan	Joy	Ted	Ed
		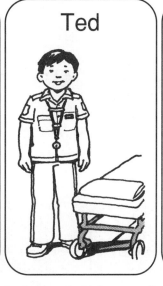	

Meet the Characters: Discuss with students the characters in the book and which careers they think are represented in these pictures.

© Steck-Vaughn Company

Building Sight Vocabulary 3, SV 6212-1

Name _____   Date _____

1   2   3   4   5

● one   two   three   four   five

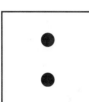 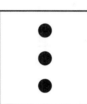 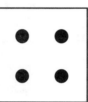 

■ one _____1_____   five _____   two _____

  two _____   four _____   four _____

  three _____   three _____   five _____

  four _____   two _____   one _____

  five _____   one _____   three _____

➡ 1 ___one___   2 _____   3 _____

  4 _____   5 _____

- - - →

two _____   _____

_____   _____

_____   _____

● Have students trace the numerals and the number words. ■ Have students write the numerals for the number words.
➡ Have them write the number word for each numeral and each set.

Lesson 1: Practice
Building Sight Vocabulary 3, SV 6212-1

Name _____   Date _____

6 7 8 9 10

six   seven   eight   nine   ten

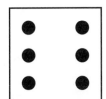 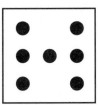 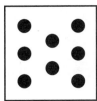 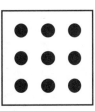 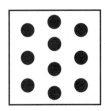

■ six ___6___   ten _____   eight _____

seven _____   nine _____   ten _____

eight _____   eight _____   six _____

nine _____   seven _____   nine _____

ten _____   six _____   seven _____

➡ 6 ___six___   7 _____   8 _____

9 _____   10 _____

- →

   seven _____

_____   _____

_____   _____

● Have students trace the numerals and the number words. ■ Have students write the numerals for the number words.
➡ Have them write the number word for each numeral and each set.

Lesson 1: Practice
Building Sight Vocabulary 3, SV 6212-1

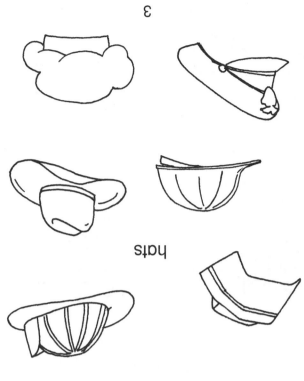

hats

Here are six hats. Make one of them white. Make two of them brown. Make three of them black.

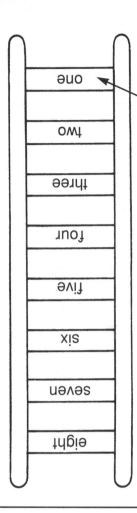

step → one
two
three
four
five
six
seven
eight

Can you go up? Put an **X** on step one. Put a ✓ on step two and on step three. Put a ○ on step four. Put a □ on step five. Put a △ on step six. Put an ← on step seven. Where is step eight?

---

brushes

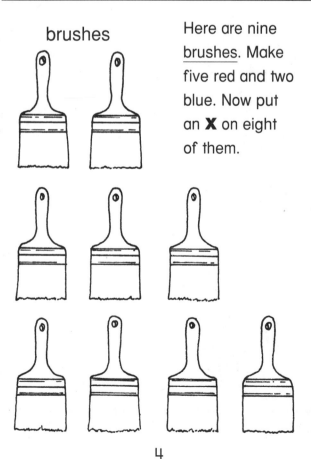

Here are nine brushes. Make five red and two blue. Now put an **X** on eight of them.

Story 1
Work with Numbers

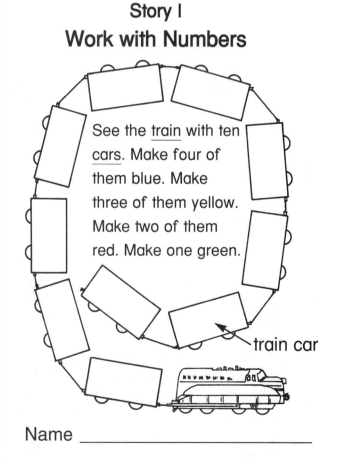

See the train with ten cars. Make four of them blue. Make three of them yellow. Make two of them red. Make one green.

train car

Name _____

After a while I took an orange ◯ to eat.

● after   while   took   an

■ after   a__ __e__   __ __ter   :   took   t__ __k

while   wh__ __ __   __ __i__e   :   an   __n

➡ a f t e r a w h i l e y o u c a n p l a y

_____

After a while you can play.

▲   look   know

took   show

low   cook   _____   _____

book   bow   _____   _____

_____   _____

★ 1. Hand me _____ orange.

2. Tell me who _____ it.

3. I will show it after a _____.

4. I will never do it again _____ this.

● Have students read the Key Sentence, read the words below, and draw a line from each word to the same word in the Key Sentence. ■ Have students write the missing letters. ➡ Each student should run a finger under the letters until a word is found. Have them put a mark between the words. They should then write the sentence on the line leaving space between each word and using capitalization and punctuation. ▲ Have students read the words in the box and write the rhyming words in the appropriate column. ★ Have students read each sentence and write one of the new words in the blank.

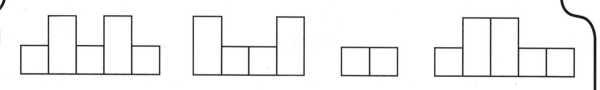

● an after while took hand back laugh again

■

➡ 1. come   over   for   a   while

Come over for a while.

2. who   took   this   from   here

▲

```
r s t o o k x b v
x l a u g h x a n
a g a i n b a c k
w h i l e h a n d
u x a f t e r x t
```

★ that's   that   is

he's   _____ _____

she's   _____ _____

it's   _____ _____

❋ 1. She's going over   comes after three?

2. What do you think   laugh together.

3. It is fun to   to him.

4. What will we   do after a while?

● Have students read each word aloud and trace it. ■ Have students look at the shape of the boxes. Have them find a word that matches the shape and print the word in the boxes. ➡ Have students write the sentences using capitalization and punctuation. ▲ Have students find and circle the words from the ● activity in the puzzle. ★ Have students write the two words that form the contractions. ❋ Have students read the sentence stem at the left and the possible endings at the right. Have them choose the ending that makes sense and draw a line to connect the two sentence parts.

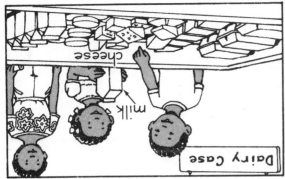

While they were there, they went to the dairy case.

"I like this," said Kim as she handed Mom some milk.

"May we get this cheese?" asked Nat. "When I had it before, I liked it better than any other kind."

"Yes, I took some, too. It was good!" said Kim.

First they went to get fruit.

"We will try these grapes. We liked them when we had them before," said Mom. She took some grapes.

"Let's get some oranges, too. We can have an orange after we play," said Nat.

After a while, he took an orange to eat.

Story 2
The Grocery

Mom wanted some things from the grocery. Kim and Nat like to help find things to eat.

After a while, Mom took Nat and Kim to the grocery. It had many good things to eat.

They saw one stocker. The stocker put many cans on shelves while they were there.

Name _____

Mom found many things to put in the cart. After a while, they took the cart to the checker.

"How much will this be?" Mom asked. Then Mom gave the checker some money.

"Come back soon!" said the checker.

Name_____ Date_____

Does a bird sing best if you hold it?

●   does   sing   best   hold

■   does   sing   best   hold

d__ __s   s__n__   be__ __   h__ __d

__oe__   s__ __ __   __ __st   h__ __ __

➡   h o l d t h i s w h i l e I s i n g

Hold this while I sing.

▲   hold   holds   holding

sing   _____   _____

laugh   _____   _____

★   1. I will hold my _____ pencil ✏ .

2. Does she _____ after me?

3. What _____ she like to sing best?

4. I want to _____ your hand.

● Have students read the Key Sentence, read the words below, and draw a line from each word to the same word in the
Key Sentence. ■ Have students write the missing letters. ➡ Each student should run a finger under the letters until a
word is found. Have them put a mark between the words. They should then write the sentence on the line leaving space
between each word and using capitalization and punctuation. ▲ Have students write the -s and -ing forms of the words.
★ Have students read each sentence and write one of the new words in the blank.

Lesson 3: Practice
Building Sight Vocabulary 3, SV 6212-1

Name _____   Date _____

● does   sing   best   hold   an   after   while   took

■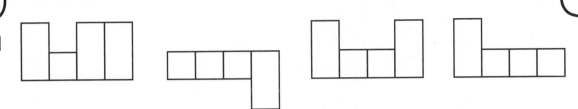

➡ 1. i   will   sing   for   you

_____

2. this   has   been   my   best   day

_____

▲   before   long   his   laugh   best
                                            back   hold
____   ____   ____   light   hand
                                            been   live
____   ____   ____   how
____   ____   ____

★   1. Can you hold   long time.

    2. It took a   her very best.

    3. He will sing   the ball 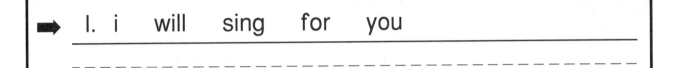 for a while?

    4. She always does   after I try to sing my best.

● Have students read each word aloud and trace it. ■ Have students look at the shape of the boxes. Have them find a word that matches the shape and print the word in the boxes. ➡ Have students write the sentences using capitalization and punctuation. ▲ Have students write the words from the box so that each column contains words with the same beginning consonant sound. ★ Have students read the sentence stem at the left and the possible endings at the right. Have them choose the ending that makes sense and draw a line to connect the two sentence parts.

Lesson 3: Practice

Building Sight Vocabulary 3, SV 6212-1

"Does a bird sing best if you hold it?" asked Dan.

"A bird likes to sing. You do not have to hold it for it to sing the best," Kate said.

"Does the bird like to do more things?" asked Mandy.

"The bird likes to walk around on a ball. It likes best to get a ride on a bike," Kate said.

Kate took one of the birds out to hold it.

"I show birds how to sing and to do things. They do them because they like to eat," said Kate. "I always give them an orange when they do the things right."

---

animal trainer

Kate

bird

"You can hold the birds. See if you can get them to sing. Give them an orange after they sing," said Kate.

Dan and Mandy got to hold the birds. The birds did sing, so they gave the birds an orange.

"You do fun work, Kate," they said. "We would like to be animal trainers, too."

Story 3
The Animal Trainer

Dad took Mandy and Dan to see some birds. The birds could do many things because of Kate. She was an animal trainer. While they were there, she showed them how she does her work.

She said, "The birds live in cages most of the time. They like it best when you hold them. It makes them happy."

cage
animal trainer
birds
Kate

Name _____

I <u>wish</u> it was <u>done</u> now. <u>Bring</u> them when I am <u>ready</u>.

●   wish   done   bring   ready

■ ready   r__ __d__   re__ __ __   **:**   wish   wi__ __

   bring   br__ __ __   __ __ __ng   **:**   done   __o__e

➡   i w i s h t h e y w o u l d b r i n g i t

_____

- -

_____

▲ couldn't   could   not

   haven't   _____   _____

   isn't   _____   _____

★   1. I haven't said my _____.

   2. I am _____ to make my wish.

   3. Tell me when you are _____ with it.

   4. He couldn't _____ them after all.

● Have students read the Key Sentences, read the words below, and draw a line from each word to the same word in the Key Sentences. ■ Have students write the missing letters. ➡ Each student should run a finger under the letters until a word is found. Have them put a mark between the words. They should then trace the sentence on the line leaving space between each word and using capitalization and punctuation. ▲ Have students write the two words that form the contractions. ★ Have students read each sentence and write one of the new words in the blank.

Name _____ Date _____

● ready bring wish done does sing best hold

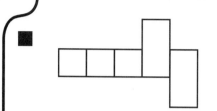 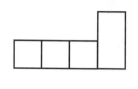 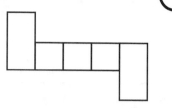

➡ get ready while I am here

▲

	s	ing
bring	brings	bringing
sing	_____	_____
hold	_____	_____
laugh	_____	_____

★ 1. I am singing my   could go, too.

2. He always brings   to make a wish?

3. I wish I   very best for you.

4. Are you ready   the pink ball .

● Have students read each word aloud and trace it. ■ Have students look at the shape of the boxes. Have them find a word that matches the shape and print the word in the boxes. ➡ Have students write the sentence using capitalization and punctuation. ▲ Have students write the -s and -ing forms of the words. ★ Have students read the sentence stem at the left and the possible endings at the right. Have them choose the ending that makes sense and draw a line to connect the two sentence parts.

electricity
switches
wire
house
Rita

"What will you do now?" asked Tony.

Rita said, "The switches are put in. After that, the lights and many things that run by electricity will be put in. Bring the wire here. I am ready."

"You work fast," said Dan. "You will be done soon."

"I wish it was done now," said Tony.

"Here are the wires. Bring them when I am ready," said Rita.

"I wish I could help," said Dan.

"Next," Rita said, "we will run wires to each light."

First, they ran wires to the house.

Rita said, "Come with me. I am ready to show you how it is done."

Tony ran to an electrician and said, "Tell us what you do."

house
Rita
wire
electrician

electrician
tools
wire
house

"I wish I could be an electrician. It would be good to use wire and all of those tools," said Dan.

"I think I would like to be an electrician, too," said Tony.

Story 4
The Electricians

"Is today the day?" asked Dan. Tony and Dan looked up and down the street.

"The workers said to be here together if we wanted to see how lights are put in," said Tony.

"I wish they would come now," said Dan. After a while Tony called, "Here they come!"

street

Name _____

Building Sight Vocabulary 3, SV 6212-1

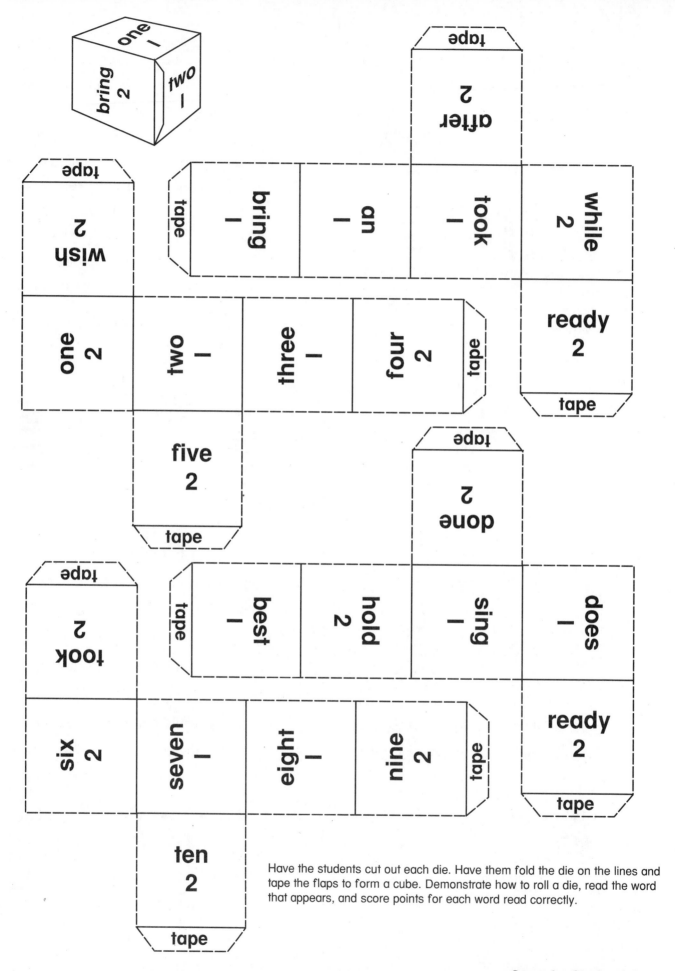

Have the students cut out each die. Have them fold the die on the lines and tape the flaps to form a cube. Demonstrate how to roll a die, read the word that appears, and score points for each word read correctly.

Game for Stories 1-4
Building Sight Vocabulary 3, SV 6212-1

Name _____   Date _____

1. I will _____ this for you.
   took   hold

2. This is the _____ work.
   back   best

3. We can _____ together.
   done   sing

4. He has _____ oranges.
   does   two

5. I was _____ for your call.
   bring   ready

6. She will _____ the light.
   hold   while

7. Make _____ wish for me.
   over   one

8. I have _____ this before.
   done   ten

9. She plays _____ she eats.
   does   after

10. He got _____ calls.
    eight   only

Have students trace the sentence and pick the missing word to complete the sentence. Have them write the missing word on the line.

Review of Stories 1-4
Building Sight Vocabulary 3, SV 6212-1

Once she told me she had nothing to read.

● once   told   nothing   read

■ told   t_ _ _   _o_ _   :   once   _nc_   on_ _

read   r_ _d   _ea_   :   nothing   no_ _ _ _ _

➡ l. thereisnothingtoread

_____

2. Itoldhertocomeatonce

_____

▲ wish + es   =   wishes

hand + ed   =   _____

read + ing   =   _____

★   l. She wishes you would _____ it.

2. I took it with me _____.

3. There is _____ brown on it.

4. He _____ me his three wishes.

● Have students read the Key Sentence, read the words below, and draw a line from each word to the same word in the Key Sentence. ■ Have students write the missing letters. ➡ Each student should run a finger under the letters until a word is found. Have them put a mark between the words. They should then write the sentence on the line leaving space between each word and using capitalization and punctuation. ▲ Have students write the root word and ending to form a new word. ★ Have students read each sentence and write one of the new words in the blank.

Lesson 5: Practice

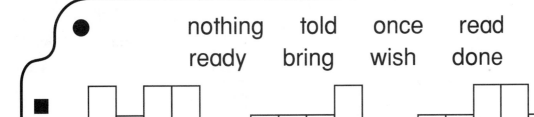

nothing   told   once   read
ready   bring   wish   done

➡   i   once   read   all   of   that

_____

- -

_____

▲

n o t h i n g x x
x t o l d d o n e
x r e a d y x x x
o n c e x r e a d
b r i n g w i s h

★

read   reading

sing   _____

hold   _____

hand   _____

laugh   _____

✳   1. Bring it when   to read.

2. Once I had a   big blue kite.

3. He told me to   it is done.

4. I have nothing   make a wish.

● Have students read each word aloud and trace it. ■ Have students look at the shape of the boxes. Have them find a word that matches the shape and print the word in the boxes. ➡ Have students write the sentence using capitalization and punctuation. ▲ Have students find and circle the words from the ● activity in the puzzle. ★ Have students write the -ing form of the words. ✳ Have students read the sentence stem at the left and the possible endings at the right. Have them choose the ending that makes sense and draw a line to connect the two sentence parts.

children

Sue

good books," Tony said.

"I wish you would read to us. You would bring children.

read or let me read to you," Sue told the bookmobile. You can take out books to

"I am happy to see you once again in the

---

bring books to all children."

to. She was not happy. Now she wants to nothing to read. There was no library to go many books. She told me that once she had that when she was little, she liked to read

Lan said," I asked Sue that, too. Sue said asked.

"Why does Sue bring books to us?" Joy

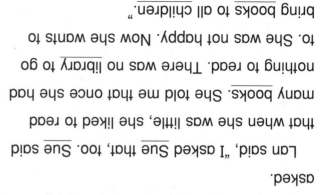

"What is the library like?" asked Joy.

"You use the library just like the bookmobile," Sue told the children. "But there are ways that the library is not like the bookmobile. The library is much bigger. There are many books."

"We like the bookmobile. We are happy that you bring books to us," said Joy.

Story 5
The Librarian

"Here is the bookmobile," said Tony. "It brings books to us on Monday. We don't have to walk to the library now when we want to read."

books

Name _____

Name _____   Date _____

| It only looks hard. | We both thank you. |

●   only   thank   both   hard

■ only   on__ __   __ __ly   ⋮   thank   th__ __ __

both   __ __th   bo__ __   ⋮   hard   h__ __d

➡   i s i t o n l y f o r m e

_____

- -

_____

▲   bring   hold   took

sing   book

look   told   _____   _____   _____

thing   cold   _____   _____   _____

★   1. Show it to _____ of them.

     2. I told you how _____ it was.

     3. She _____ read it once.

     4. She told him, " _____ you very much."

● Have students read the Key Sentences, read the words below, and draw a line from each word to the same word in the Key Sentences. ■ Have students write the missing letters. ➡ Each student should run a finger under the letters until a word is found. Have them put a mark between the words. They should then write the sentence on the line leaving a space between each word and using capitalization and punctuation. ▲ Have students write the words from the box so that each column contains words that rhyme. ★ Have students read each sentence and write one of the new words in the blank.

Lesson 6: Practice
Building Sight Vocabulary 3, SV 6212-1

Name _____   Date _____

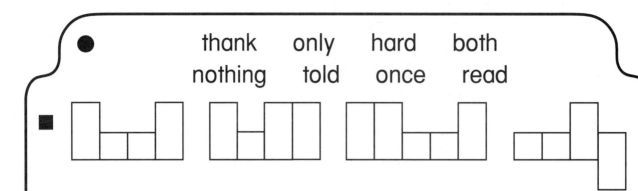

● thank   only   hard   both

nothing   told   once   read

➡ thank   you   very   much

_____

- -

_____

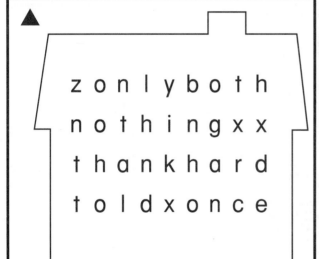

▲

z o n l y b o t h
n o t h i n g x x
t h a n k h a r d
t o l d x o n c e

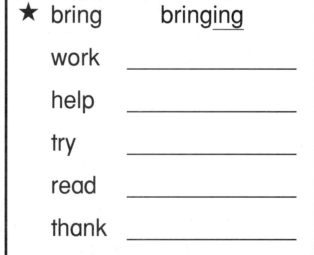

★ bring   bringing

work   _____

help   _____

try   _____

read   _____

thank   _____

� 1. Have you read   to thank you.

2. Both of you   that long book  ?

3. I am only trying   can read this.

● Have students read each word aloud and trace it. ■ Have students look at the shape of the boxes. Have them find a word that matches the shape and print the word in the boxes. ➡ Have students write the sentence using capitalization and punctuation. ▲ Have students find and circle the words from the ● activity in the puzzle. ★ Have students write the -ing form of the words. ✷ Have students read the sentence stem at the left and the possible endings at the right. Have them choose the ending that makes sense and draw a line to connect the two sentence parts.

Lesson 6: Practice
Building Sight Vocabulary 3, SV 6212-1

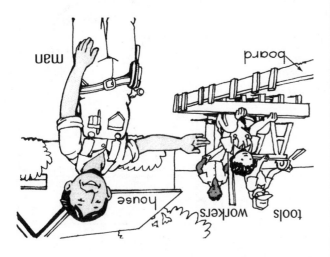

"These workers here work for me. They use their tools," said the man. "Today we are cutting these boards and putting them here. It will show you how big the house is going to be."

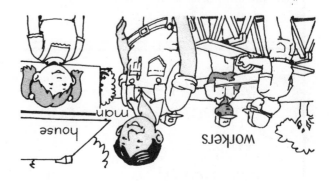

"Why do you want to put your house here?" Mandy asked.

"This is not my house. I only help to make this house. I am here to see that the workers do the right work. I must see what goes into making the house," he said.

"It looks like it is hard to make a house," said Kim.

"It only looks hard," the man said.

Kim said, "The new house looks little."

The man laughed and said, "You may think that at first. If you come back after a while, you will see how big the house will be."

"We will," said Mandy. "We both thank you. It was fun to see your work."

Story 6
The Building Contractor

Mandy and Kim are riding their bikes. On the way to play, they see many workers. They both stop to see what the workers are doing.

A man said, "Would you like to see what we do? We are going to work hard to put a new house here. Why don't you both come see?"

Name _____

● They <u>thought</u> of it as their very <u>own</u> place.

He <u>goes</u> there <u>every</u> day.

thought   own   every   place   goes

■   i t h o u g h t i t w a s m y o w n

_____

- -

_____

➡ can not   hasn't
   has not   can't
   was not   isn't
   can not   can't
   is not   wasn't

▲ <u>e</u>very   I. <u>after</u>

   <u>d</u>one   2. _____

   <u>b</u>ring   3. _____

   <u>a</u>fter   4. _____

★ I. _____ car 🚗 isn't big.

   2. Nat goes to the right _____ every time.

   3. The train _____ by the same place.

   4. I _____ it wasn't right.

   5. I _____ the big dog 🐕 .

● Have students read the Key Sentences, read the words below, and draw a line from each word to the same word in the Key Sentences. ■ Each student should run a finger under the letters until a word is found. Have them put a mark between the words. They should then write the sentence on the line leaving a space between each word and using capitalization and punctuation. ➡ Have students draw lines to match the two words that form the contractions. ▲ Have students write the words in alphabetical order. ★ Have students read each sentence and write one of the new words in the blank.

Name _____ Date _____

every   goes   own   place   thought

Lan Every cat	goes runs	to that place after me

_____

- -

_____

➡ every + one   =   _____

every + thing   =   _____

every + where =   _____

▲ put   put ⊥ ing   cut _____

get _____   let _____

★ 1. Everyone goes   to my place to eat.

2. I thought you   had your own.

3. I thought   goes together.

4. Everything   it was over here.

● Have students read each word aloud and trace it. ■ Have students choose a phrase from each box and then read the sentence. Students trace the sentence on the line. ➡ Have students combine the two words to form compound words. ▲ Have students double the consonants to make the *-ing* form of the words. ★ Have students read the sentence stem at the left and the possible endings at the right. Have them choose the ending that makes sense and draw a line to connect the two sentence parts.

Lesson 7: Practice

Building Sight Vocabulary 3, SV 6212-1

place to be sold."

Mandy ran up to them and said, "I know we don't own this place, but we come here every day to play. We never wanted this

"Sold."

One day soon after that some people came. They put up a new sign. It said,

was going to own their good place to play.

The girls thought about the sign and who fun. Now we can't play here every day."

"Oh, no!" said Mandy. "There goes all our place is for sale," she said.

Kim thought and thought. "It says that this

"Some people thought it would make a good place to live, too. Now they own it," said the woman. "They will put a new house here. You can't play here now. But you can come back every day and see what goes on. I think you will like to see the work on the new house."

The girls thought that they would like it, too.

Story 7
The Real Estate Agent

Every day Mandy goes to play with Lan and Kim. Tip likes to play, too. He goes every day. They know a good place to play. They thought of it as their very own place.

One day there was something new in their place to play.

"What does it say? Can you read it?" asked Lan.

Name _____

Name _____   Date _____

Each worker has a part to build.   Which other places?

●   build   part   each   which   other

■   _____ w h i c h p a r t c a n y o u b u i l d _____

    -

    _____

➡   some + one   =   _____

   some + where   =   _____

▲ build   building   builder

   work   _____   _____

   own   _____   _____

★   l. Who had the _____ two books ?

   2. _____ part are you building?

   3. There is a builder for each _____ .

   4. Put the shoes 👟 by _____ other.

   5. Each worker has something to _____ .

● Have students read the Key Sentences, read the words below, and draw a line from each word to the same word in the Key Sentences. ■ Each student should run a finger under the letters until a word is found. Have them put a mark between the words. They should then write the sentence on the line leaving a space between each word and using capitalization and punctuation. ➡ Have students combine the two words to form compound words. ▲ Have students write the -ing and -er forms of the words. ★ Have students read each sentence and write one of the new words in the blank.

© Steck-Vaughn Company   31   **Lesson 8: Practice**
Building Sight Vocabulary 3, SV 6212-1

● build   each   part   other   which

every   goes   own   place   thought

■

| Which one Which part | do you want is better | to build in each place |

_____

- -

_____

➡ any + thing   =   _____

any + where   =   _____

any + one   =   _____

▲ come̸   *coming*   place   _____

use   _____   live   _____

★ 1. The other part   in that new place?

2. Is anyone living   goes with this.

3. I thought he had   will you build?

4. Which part   his own place.

● Have students read each word aloud and trace it. ■ Have students choose a phrase from each box and then write the sentence on the line. ➡ Have students combine the two words to form compound words. ▲ Have students cross out the *e* in each word and write the *-ing* form of the words. ★ Have students read the sentence stem at the left and the possible endings at the right. Have them choose the ending that makes sense and draw a line to connect the two sentence parts.

"pipes to put in those places."

there is going to be water. We know which of the pipes will go to a place in which

"We know where each pipe goes. Each

"Then we will put other pipes in."

the house, we will come back," said Ann.

"After other workers build other parts of

the ground. They will be under the house."

Ann said, "First, we put the pipes under

"Which other places?" asked Eric.

in many other places."

a part to build. Our part is to put in the pipes

Ann told Eric and Rose, "Each worker has

Ann said, "These are our tools. We know

which ones to use so each pipe is put

together right."

"We both want to see how you do it," said

Rose.

"We will show you," said Ann.

"Thank you," said Rose and Eric.

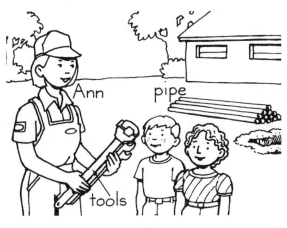

4

Story 8
The Plumber

Eric and Rose each thought it would be fun

to see how workers build a house. So, they

went to where building was going on.

Eric said to the workers, "I thought we were

going to see a house! Are you going to build it

today?"

Name _____

Name _____   Date _____

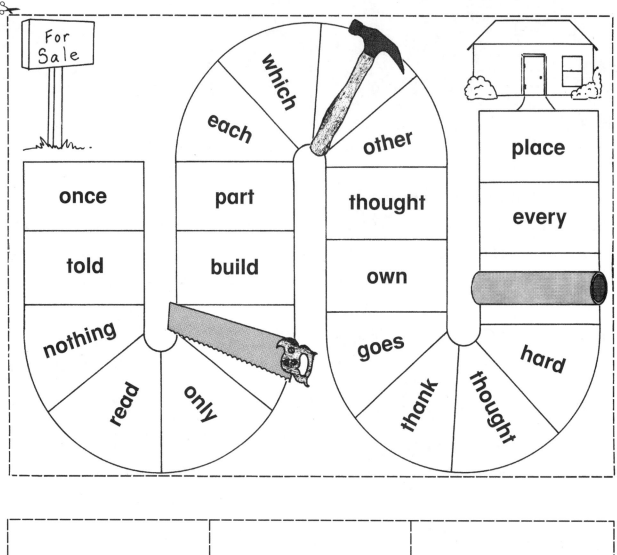

1	2	3
4	5	6

Have students cut out the game board and cards. They paste the game board on construction paper. Students lay the pile of numbered cards face down. Using buttons or markers, they take turns drawing a card and moving the number of spaces shown. They read the word they land on. If they say the word incorrectly, they lose their next turn. The first player to the house wins.

© Steck-Vaughn Company

Game for Stories 5-8
Building Sight Vocabulary 3, SV 6212-1

1. Kim _____ out each day.
   goes   own

2. I go _____ day, too.
   place   every

3. I will _____ a big place.
   build   other

4. We do our _____ work.
   nothing   own

5. We _____ do our part.
   each   which

6. I _____ you to come here.
   read   told

7. We _____ have one.
   only   once

8. We both work very _____.
   hard   both

9. I have done _____ today.
   ready   nothing

10. I saw it _____ before.
    only   once

Have students trace the sentence and pick the missing word to complete the sentence. Have them write the missing word on the line.

Be sure to come the next day to see more than this.

●   than   more   next   sure

■   i h a v e m o r e t h a n y o u d o

_____

— —

_____

➡ hard   harder   long   _____

    work   _____   sing   _____

    fast   _____   own   _____

▲ big   big g er   cut   _____

    run   _____   stop   _____

★   1. Does she sing _____ than I do?

     2. He is bigger _____ both of us!

     3. Can you run faster _____ time?

     4. You _____ work harder than I do.

● Have students read the Key Sentence, read the words below, and draw a line from each word to the same word in the Key Sentence. ■ Each student should run a finger under the letters until a word is found. Have them put a mark between the words. They should then write the sentence on the line leaving a space between each word and using capitalization and punctuation. ➡ Have students write the -er form of the words. ▲ Have students double the consonants to make the -ing form of the words. ★ Have students read each sentence and write one of the new words in the blank.

Name _____   Date _____

●   which   other   part   each   build

than   more   next   sure

■

| Each day
Each time | we cut more
I ran more | than they did
than the other |

_____

_ _

_____

➡

w h i c h e k t h a n
e s u r e u m o r e b
o t h e r t a n e x t

▲ every + thing   =   _____

some + thing   =   _____

any + thing   =   _____

★   I. He is sure to   more green in it?

2. Which one has   than you can.

3. I can jump more times   do it next time.

4. Which part will   you sing next?

● Have students read each word aloud and trace it. ■ Have students choose a phrase from each box and then write the sentence on the line. ➡ Have students find and circle the words from the ● activity in the puzzle. ▲ Have students combine the two words to form compound words. ★ Have students read the sentence stem at the left and the possible endings at the right. Have them choose the ending that makes sense and draw a line to connect the two sentence parts.

Lesson 9: Practice

Building Sight Vocabulary 3, SV 6212-1

Story 9
The Carpenters

The carpenters came the next day.

Tony asked, "Which part of the house will you work on next?"

"We will build many parts of the house," Mack said.

"Is your work harder than the others?" Tony asked him.

"No, we just have more things to do than they do," Mack said.

Name _____

"First those carpenters must be sure where each part goes. Next we will build the frame of the house. Then you can tell what the house is going to look like," said Mack. Some workers were cutting boards. They had to be sure the boards were cut just right. Other workers were building the frame.

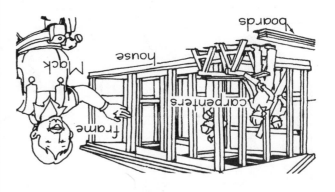

Mack said, "We each have some of our own hand tools. Those tools over there are for us to use, too."

Tony said, "This house is bigger than I thought it would be. It looked so little before!"

"Be sure to come the next day to see more than this," said Mack.

The next day Tony and Dan were back again. More of the house was done. The roof was on. Next the windows and doors will be put in.

"This house is going up faster than I thought. I thought for sure there was more to building a house than this," said Tony.

Name _____   Date _____

They should pick out any kind before we start.

●   kind   should   pick   start

■   p i c k t h e k i n d y o u w a n t

_____

- -

_____

➡ start   starts   started   starting

    pick   _____   _____   _____

    part   _____   _____   _____

▲ own   owner   owners

    help   _____   _____

    build   _____   _____

    own   _____   _____

★   I. What _____ are they picking?

    2. You _____ start right now.

    3. It was kind of you to _____ helping.

    4. _____ the kind you want.

● Have students read the Key Sentence, read the words below, and draw a line from each word to the same word in the Key Sentence. ■ Each student should run a finger under the letters until a word is found. Have them put a mark between the words. They should then write the sentence on the line leaving a space between each word and using capitalization and punctuation. ➡ Have students write the -s, -ed, and -ing forms of the words. ▲ Have students write the -er and -ers forms of the words. ★ Have students read each sentence and write one of the new words in the blank.

Name _____   Date _____

■

| The four birds | should start | to go |
| The five girls | are sure | to sing |

_____

- -

_____

➡

s h o u l d		k i n d o
o o m o r e		s t a r t
s u r e x e		k p i c k
e n e x t c		d t h a n

▲ would + nøt =   wouldn't

could + nøt = _____

should + nøt = _____

★ 1. We couldn't   to your cat 🐱 .

2. Say kind things   start over again.

3. Did Mandy pick   say to them?

4. What should I   more than Lan?

● Have students read each word aloud and trace it. ■ Have students choose a phrase from each box and then write the sentence on the line. ➡ Have students find and circle the words from the ● activity in the puzzle. ▲ Have students combine the two words to form contractions. ★ Have students read the sentence stem at the left and the possible endings at the right. Have them choose the ending that makes sense and draw a line to connect the two sentence parts.

Story 10
The Painters

Lan went by to pick up Rose. They started walking down the street. Lan and Rose saw some workers.

"What kind of work will they do?" Lan said.

"We should go ask before they start," Rose said.

Name _____

"What kind of work do you do?" Lan asked.

"We are painters. We are about to start. Some of us will start to work out here. I have picked others who will go in and work there. We have our own kind of work to do. We will paint every part of the house," said a painter.

"May we help you pick out the yellow paint?" asked Lan.

"Oh, no. The owners have picked it out. They should pick out any kind before we start. Let me show you. The owners picked pretty paint for each part of the house," said the painter.

"Here is a brush I use in my work. With the right kind of brush I can be sure to do a good work," she said as she picked up a big brush.

"I like your kind of work. I sure wish I could paint something, " said Rose.

"We should go home and get out paints. We can play like we are painters. I can think of all kinds of things we can paint," said Lan.

"Let's get started. That will be fun," said Rose.

Name _____   Date _____

I think you <u>set</u> out <u>enough</u> <u>small</u> ones to <u>grow</u>.

grow   enough   set   small

■   a s m a l l d o g   w i l l g r o w b i g

_____

— —

_____

➡ grow   grows   grow<u>ing</u>

pick   _____   _____

start   _____   _____

build   _____   _____

▲ take   _taking_   ▲   use   _____

give   _____   ▲   live   _____

★   l. I will set out two _____ flowers .

2. They will start growing soon _____ .

3. They will _____ big enough.

4. Look at my new _____ of skates .

● Have students read the Key Sentence, read the words below, and draw a line from each word to the same word in the Key Sentence. ■ Each student should run a finger under the letters until a word is found. Have them put a mark between the words. They should then write the sentence on the line leaving a space between each word and using capitalization and punctuation. ➡ Have students write the -s and -ing forms of the words. ▲ Have students cross out the e in each word and write the -ing form of the words. ★ Have students read each sentence and write one of the new words in the blank.

Lesson 11: Practice
Building Sight Vocabulary 3, SV 6212-1

grow   enough   set   small

kind   should   pick   start

■

| A small dog 🐕
The yellow cat 🐈 | started to
should | eat
grow |

_____

- -

_____

➡ every + thing   = _____

every + one   = _____

every + where   = _____

▲ set   set ┼ ing   ▲ cut   _____

stop   _____   ▲ put   _____

★   1. This cat 🐈   grow big enough?

2. Will it   three small apples 🍎🍎🍎 ?

3. It should grow   is kind of small.

4. Can you pick   if it eats enough.

● Have students read each word aloud and trace it. ■ Have students choose a phrase from each box and then write the sentence on the line. ➡ Have students combine the two words to form compound words. ▲ Have students double the consonants to make the -ing form of the words. ★ Have students read the sentence stem at the left and the possible endings at the right. Have them choose the ending that makes sense and draw a line to connect the two sentence parts.

Story II
The Landscaper

Jenny saw someone with small <u>trees</u> by a <u>house</u>.

Jenny asked, "Will those grow there?"

"With enough <u>water</u> and <u>sun</u>, all of these things will grow," said the <u>landscaper</u>. "I picked the kind of <u>trees</u> to set here."

Jenny said, "They will look pretty."

Name _____

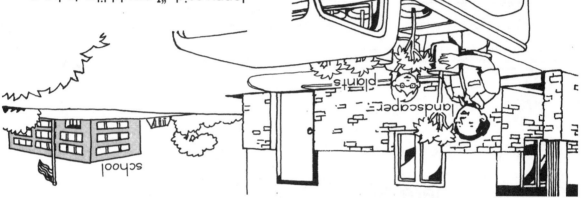

"I set out small <u>plants</u>," the <u>landscaper</u> told her. "Soon they will grow big. It is fun to pick out the kind of <u>plants</u> that will grow best."

"I think you set out enough small ones to grow. The plants will make this place pretty!" said Jenny.

2

Jenny said, "I would like to be a <u>landscaper</u> when I grow up."

"I wanted to be one, too, when I was small," he told Jenny. "I used to grow all kinds of things.

"When you are big enough, you can go to school just as I did. Someone will show you how to grow things. You will know how to set <u>plants</u> so they will grow best."

3

He let Jenny help him set out a small <u>tree</u>.

"As this <u>tree</u> grows big, you will grow big," the <u>landscaper</u> told her.

Jenny will go by every day to see the small <u>tree</u> grow. She knows that one day it will grow big.

4

Name _____ Date _____

We <u>carry</u> and <u>leave</u> it when it is <u>hot</u> or <u>cold</u>.

●   carry   cold   hot   leave

■   c a n y o u c a r r y a l l o f t h e s e

_____

- -

_____

➡ gr<u>ow</u>   hot   day

    g<u>ot</u>   show   should

    ma<u>y</u>   would   not

    c<u>ould</u>   stay   know

▲ hot   does   1. <u>cold</u>   4. _____

   cold   first   2. _____   5. _____

   each   grow   3. _____   6. _____

★   1. What time do you have to _____ ?

    2. Take your coat off if you are _____ .

    3. Will you _____ two orange books ?

    4. Put your coat on if you are _____ .

● Have students read the Key Sentence, read the words below, and draw a line from each word to the same word in the Key Sentence. ■ Each student should run a finger under the letters until a word is found. Have them put a mark between the words. They should then write the sentence on the line leaving a space between each word and using capitalization and punctuation. ➡ Have students draw lines to match the rhyming words. ▲ Have students write the words in alphabetical order. ★ Have students read each sentence and write one of the new words in the blank.

Lesson 12: Practice

    Building Sight Vocabulary 3, SV 6212-1

Name _____ Date _____

carry   hot   cold   leave

small   set   grow   enough

■

| I will carry | cold milk 🥛 | for you |
| I can leave | hot soup 🍜 | with him |

_____

_ _

_____

➡ some + time   = _____

any + where   = _____

every + thing   = _____

▲ carry   _____   ⏶ carried   _____

carries   _____   ⏶ carrying   _____

★   1. I will leave because   will grow big.

2. Can you carry   it is too hot.

3. Set it down   in these brown leaves.

4. The small one   a small basket ?

● Have students read each word aloud and trace it. ■ Have students choose a phrase from each box and then write the sentence on the line. ➡ Have students combine the two words to form compound words. ▲ Show students how the word *carry* changes with each ending. Have students write the *-es, -ed,* and *-ing* forms of the word. ★ Have students read the sentence stem at the left and the possible endings at the right. Have them choose the ending that makes sense and draw a line to connect the two sentence parts.

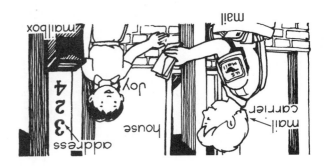

"It is so hot today. I would not like to carry mail when it is hot," said Joy. "It would be better to carry it when it is cold."

"We carry and leave it when it is hot and when it is cold. I like it better when it is not this hot," said the mail carrier.

"I always leave mail in a mailbox," said the mail carrier.

"How do you know where to leave our mail?" asked Joy.

"I saw the 324 on your house. All mail must have an address. We carry the mail to that address. We leave it there," she said.

"Would you like a cold drink?" asked Joy.

"That would be good on this hot day," said the mail carrier.

The mail carrier said, "I must leave now. I have mail to carry."

"I am happy that you will carry our mail," said Joy.

"I will see you again," said the mail carrier as she walked away.

Story 12
The Mail Carrier

The mail carrier stopped at the house. Joy came out.

"I was going to leave you some mail," the mail carrier said.

"Do you always carry our mail?" asked Joy.

"I carry the mail around here. There are other mail carriers who carry mail in other places," she said.

Name _____

Name _____   Date _____

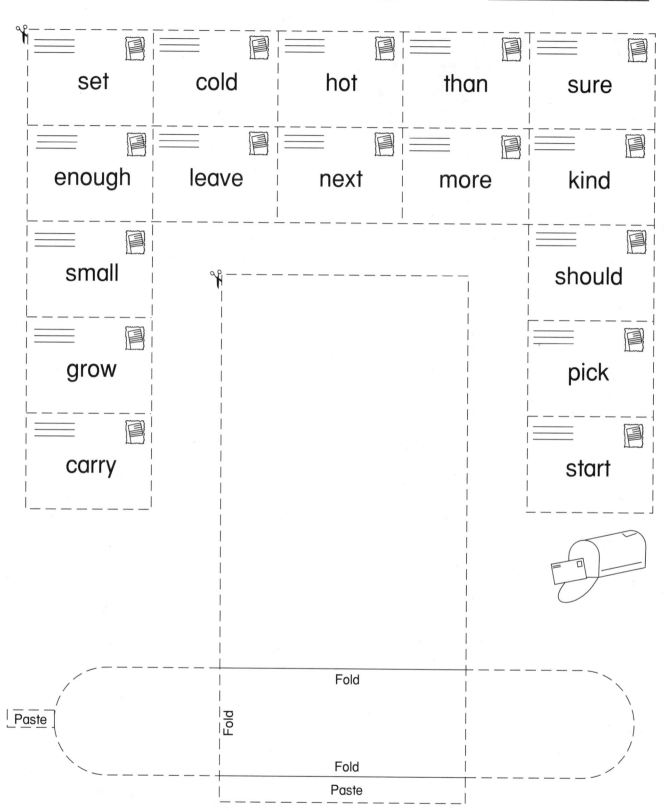

set

cold

hot

than

sure

enough

leave

next

more

kind

small

should

grow

pick

carry

start

Fold

Fold

Fold

Paste

Paste

Have students cut out the mailbox and assemble it using the illustration as a guide. Have students cut out the letters. Playing the game in small groups, one student is the mail carrier and holds the pile of letters face down. Students take turns rolling a die. The mail carrier takes that number of letters and places them in the student's mailbox. They then read their "mail." If a word is read incorrectly, the student must return the letter to the mail carrier. When all letters have been given out, the student with the most mail wins.

Game for Stories 9-12
Building Sight Vocabulary 3, SV 6212-1

1. Four is more _____ two.
   sure   than

2. Which _____ should I pick?
   kind   than

3. You did _____ work than I.
   more   start

4. Are you sure I am _____?
   than   next

5. You _____ a time to start.
   next   pick

6. I can carry _____ for us.
   enough   leave

7. I will _____ a small set.
   small   carry

8. It is too _____ out here.
   cold   enough

9. It will not _____ in the cold.
   hot   grow

10. Did you _____ it down?
    small   set

Have students trace the sentence and pick the missing word to complete the sentence. Have them write the missing word on the line.

Name _____ Date _____

It will not <u>hurt</u> to <u>stay</u> and <u>sleep</u>. | <u>Sit</u> right here.

●   hurt   sit   stay   sleep

■   s t a y a n d g o t o s l e e p n o w

_____

- -

_____

➡ live   live<u>s</u>   liv<u>ed</u>

   use   _____   _____

   time   _____   _____

   live   _____   _____

   like   _____   _____

▲   l. _____ here and hold my hand.

   2. At eight it is time to go to _____.

   3. I used to _____ by him.

   4. Stay here and you will not get _____.

● Have students read the Key Sentences, read the words below, and draw a line from each word to the same word in the Key Sentences. ■ Each student should run a finger under the letters until a word is found. Have them put a mark between the words. They should then write the sentence on the line leaving a space between each word and using capitalization and punctuation. ➡ Have students write the -s and -ed forms of the words. ▲ Have students read each sentence and write one of the new words in the blank.

Lesson 13: Practice
Building Sight Vocabulary 3, SV 6212-1

Name _____   Date _____

hurt   sit   sleep   stay

leave   hot   cold   carry

■

Kim will sit	there	when you leave
Jenny can sleep	on it	if she is cold

_____

_ _

➡

t s i t a h o t s l e e p

o c o l d s t a y l h u r t

t l e a v e e e c a r r y r

▲ with + in   =   _____

with + out   =   _____

day + time   =   _____

★ 1. We will leave in   not stay green.

2. The leaves will   of them leave?

3. Did the four   the daytime.

4. I never sit   where it is hot.

● Have students read each word aloud and trace it. ■ Have students choose a phrase from each box and then write the sentence on the line. ➡ Have students find and circle the words from the ● activity in the puzzle. ▲ Have students combine the two words to form compound words. ★ Have students read the sentence stem at the left and the possible endings at the right. Have them choose the ending that makes sense and draw a line to connect the two sentence parts.

© Steck-Vaughn Company

Lesson 13: Practice

Building Sight Vocabulary 3, SV 6212-1

While Ed and Ted were sitting there, they saw some people who were hurt. Someone looked like he was sleeping. They saw workers helping the hurt people.

Ted and Ed saw some nurses working while they were sitting there. Some nurses were leaving to get some sleep. Some other nurses were coming to work.

Workers are at the hospital all of the time. Many workers stay at the hospital in the daytime. Some workers stay at other times.

Some workers like night work better than working in the day. They have to sleep in the daytime. There is a place for workers to eat in the hospital, but there is no place to sleep.

Interns stay at the hospital for a long time. Sometimes they eat and sleep at the hospital. The interns must be there to help those who get hurt.

Ed and Ted wanted to stay longer at the hospital. "We would like to come back again and see more," they said.

Story 13
The Hospital Workers

Ted and Ed's dad took them to the hospital. He works there. They stopped at the emergency entrance and went in.

"Those who are hurt stay and sleep here. Stay here while I go see about something. We are not going to stay long. Sit right here," Dad told them.

Name _____

| Keep his hand clean to make it well. | Take most of it. |

●   keep   clean   well   most

■   i c a n k e e p m o s t o f t h e m

_____

— —

_____

➡ let us   I'm   let us   she's

   I am   we're   she is   he's

   we are   let's   he is   let's

▲ stay   stays   stayed   staying

   clean   _____   _____   _____

   show   _____   _____   _____

★   1. How _____ does Kim sing?

    2. She sings well _____ of the time.

    3. Did you put on _____ socks ?

    4. _____ your hands clean.

● Have students read the Key Sentences, read the words below, and draw a line from each word to the same word in the Key Sentences. ■ Each student should run a finger under the letters until a word is found. Have them put a mark between the words. They should then write the sentence on the line leaving a space between each word and using capitalization and punctuation. ➡ Have students draw lines to match the two words with the contraction. ▲ Have students write the -s, -ed, and -ing forms of the words. ★ Have students read each sentence and write one of the new words in the blank.

clean   keep   most   well

stay   sleep   sit   hurt

■

| Dan can
Lan will | clean the house
stay in bed | now
today |

_____

- -

_____

➡ has + not = hasn't   was + not = _____

is + not   = _____   had + not = _____

have + not = _____   can + not = _____

▲ 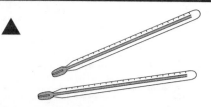   s k e e p o c l e a n p h u r t
                           i k k m o s t m h t s s l e e p
                           t w l w e l l w d t s t a y l l

★ 1. Most of them   enough sleep.

   2. It will not hurt   to stay clean.

   3. I have had   of the red ones.

   4. You must keep most   grow well here.

● Have students read each word aloud and trace it. ■ Have students choose a phrase from each box and then write the sentence on the line. ➡ Have students combine the two words to form contractions. ▲ Have students find and circle the words from the ● activity in the puzzle. ★ Have students read the sentence stem at the left and the possible endings at the right. Have them choose the ending that makes sense and draw a line to connect the two sentence parts.

Story 14
The Doctor

Eric's mom said, "Eric, will you keep the <u>cat</u> out of the <u>tree</u>? It keeps going up the <u>tree</u>."

Eric ran under the big <u>tree</u>. The <u>cat</u> played there most of the time. Eric jumped for the <u>cat</u>.

"Oh!" said Eric. "I hurt my hand!"

"That cut does not look good," said Mom. "We should get some help."

Name _____

Mom took Eric to see the doctor.

"Eric, have you been staying well?" asked Dr. Brown.

"Pretty well. Today I'm not too good. My hand hurts. It is kind of hot. Can you make it better again?" asked Eric.

"Let me look at it," said Dr. Brown.

2

Mom had put a bandage on Eric's cut to keep it clean. First, Dr. Brown took the <u>bandage</u> off.

Dr. Brown looked at Eric's hand and said, "This is a clean cut. It should be well in no time."

She cleaned it out again. She put <u>medicine</u> on it. Then she put a clean <u>bandage</u> on it.

"It looks good," Dr. Brown said.

3

"I will give you a <u>shot</u>," said Dr. Brown. "I will make sure your cut gets well."

After the <u>shot</u>, <u>Dr. Brown</u> said to Eric's mom, "Keep his hand clean to make it well. Here is <u>medicine</u> for Eric. Have him take most of it. Then come back and see me. It should be well by then."

4

Name _____   Date _____

Do you <u>ever</u> <u>hurry</u> to help one in <u>need</u>?   Ask <u>another</u> time.

●   ever   hurry   need   another

■   I n e e d a n o t h e r b o o k

_____

— —

_____

➡ need   need<u>s</u>   need<u>ed</u>   need<u>ing</u>

clean   _____   _____   _____

stay   _____   _____   _____

▲ hurry   hurry _____   carry   carry _____

hurries _____   carries _____

hurried _____   carried _____

★   I. You _____ to hurry and get one.

2. I have _____ blue one you would like.

3. We needed to _____ back.

4. Did they _____ get it clean?

● Have students read the Key Sentences, read the words below, and draw a line from each word to the same word in the Key Sentences. ■ Each student should run a finger under the letters until a word is found. Have them put a mark between the words. They should then write the sentence on the line leaving a space between each word and using capitalization and punctuation. ➡ Have students write the -s, -ed, and -ing forms of the words. ▲ Have students trace each form of the words *carry* and *hurry*. Help them see that the *y* is changed to *i* when -es or -ed is added. ★ Have students read each sentence and write one of the new words in the blank.

© Steck-Vaughn Company   Building Sight Vocabulary 3, SV 6212-1

Name _____ Date _____

need   hurry   ever   another

well   most   keep   clean

■

| We | always hurry | to clean up |
| They | never need | to paint |

_____

— —

_____

➡ any + one   = _____

some + one   = _____

some + time   = _____

▲ help   help_er_   ▲ small   _____

clean   _____   ▲ start   _____

★ 1. I will keep nine   all day.

2. This is cleaner   than the blue one.

3. You need to stay   had a smaller car  ?

4. Have you ever   red balloons .

● Have students read each word aloud and trace it. ■ Have students choose a phrase from each box and then write the sentence on the line. ➡ Have students combine the two words to form compound words. ▲ Have students write the -er form of the words. ★ Have students read the sentence stem at the left and the possible endings at the right. Have them choose the ending that makes sense and draw a line to connect the two sentence parts.

Lesson 15: Practice
Building Sight Vocabulary 3, SV 6212-1

"Do you ever help people?" Ted asked.

"We hurry to help whoever is in need," Nat's mom said. "We help children find their way home. We try to keep people from hurting each other. We are never in too much of a hurry to help those in need."

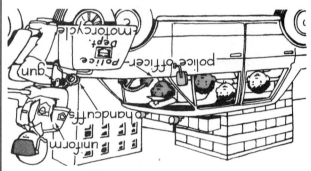

"Do you ever ride a motorcycle?" Ted asked.

"No, I don't ever need to ride one," she said. "You can tell most police officers by our uniforms. We carry handcuffs. Another thing we carry is a gun. Most of the time we have no need for one. But we will use it if we ever need to."

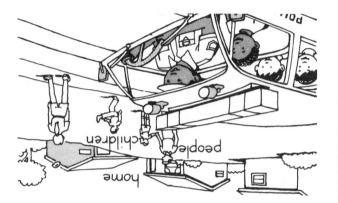

"Another thing I do is go to schools," said Nat's mom. "I tell children how police can help them."

"May we go for one more ride?" asked Ed.

"No, I have to go. Ask another time. I will be happy to take you," said Nat's mom.

"Thank you. We would like that," Ted said.

Story 15
The Police Officer

Nat's mom is a police officer. She wanted to give Nat, Ted, and Ed a ride in her police car.

"Hurry up and get in," said Nat. "My mom works with traffic. She helps people as they hurry to work. If they are ever in too much of a hurry, she stops them."

Name _____

| I lost two. | I also don't want you to pull any this year. |

pull   also   year   lost

■   i a l s o l o s t m y h a t

_____

– –

_____

➡ pull   pulls   pulled   pulling

clean   _____   _____   _____

need   _____   _____   _____

stay   _____   _____   _____

pull   _____   _____   _____

start   _____   _____   _____

▲ 1. _____ your blue wagon over here.

2. I _____ pulled my red wagon here.

3. I thought you had _____ it.

4. Will you be seven next _____?

● Have students read the Key Sentences, read the words below, and draw a line from each word to the same word in the Key Sentences. ■ Each student should run a finger under the letters until a word is found. Have them put a mark between the words. They should then write the sentence on the line leaving a space between each word and using capitalization and punctuation. ➡ Have students write the -s, -ed, and -ing forms of the words. ▲ Have students read each sentence and write one of the new words in the blank.

Name _____   Date _____

●   also   lost   pull   year

         another   ever   hurry   need

■

| One tooth 🦷
 A wagon | was lost <br> was pulled | this year <br> today |

_____

- -

_____

➡ with + out   =   _____

    with + in   =   _____

    up + on   =   _____

▲ can't   have not   don't   can not

   isn't   can not   can't   should not

   haven't   is not   shouldn't   do not

★   l. I lost another one   where I lost it.

    2. I don't know   need help?

    3. Do you ever   this year.

    4. She also   got her wish.

● Have students read each word aloud and trace it. ■ Have students choose a phrase from each box and then write the sentence on the line. ➡ Have students combine the two words to form compound words. ▲ Have students draw lines to match the two words that form the contractions. ★ Have students read the sentence stem at the left and the possible endings at the right. Have them choose the ending that makes sense and draw a line to connect the two sentence parts.

© Steck-Vaughn Company

Lesson 16: Practice
Building Sight Vocabulary 3, SV 6212-1

Story 16
The Dentist

Each year Mandy goes to the dentist. This year Mandy had lost two teeth.

Once before, the dentist had pulled one of her teeth. Mandy didn't want him to pull another one this year.

Name_____

The dentist said, "It is good to see you again this year. Have you lost any teeth?"

Mandy said, "I lost two! I also don't want you to pull any this year."

The dentist said, "Did your teeth grow much this year?"

"I have some new ones," she said.

"Your teeth look good," said the dentist. "I will not have to pull any!"

The dentist told Mandy what she should eat. He also showed Mandy how to clean her teeth.

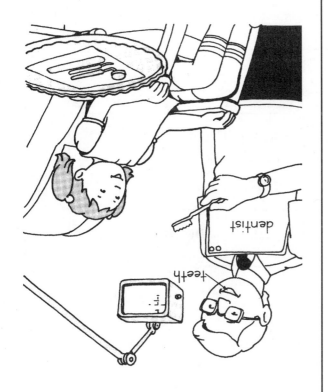

"Mandy, keep your teeth clean and come back to see me next year!" said the dentist. "Here is a toothbrush to keep, also."

"Thank you," she said. "I'll see you next year!"

Name_____   Date_____

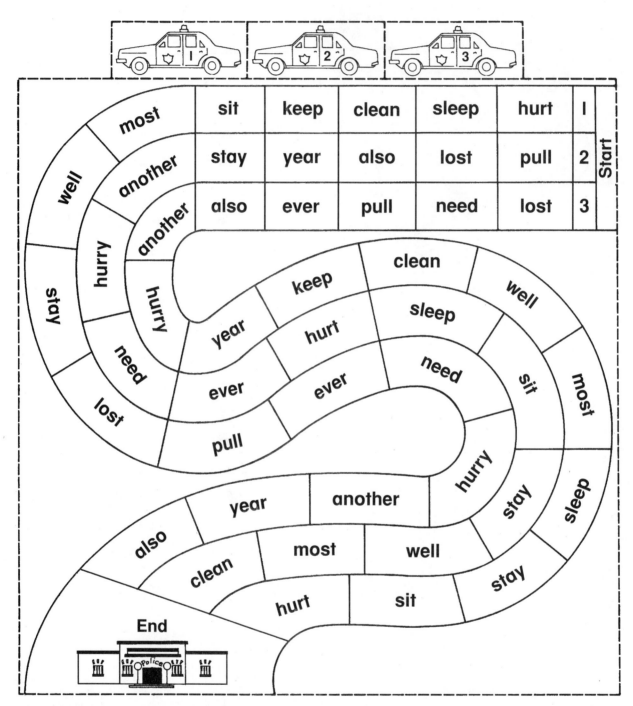

The game board contains the following words:

Start column (right side, top to bottom rows 1, 2, 3):

sit	keep	clean	sleep	hurt	1
stay	year	also	lost	pull	2
also	ever	pull	need	lost	3

Path words: most, another, another, well, hurry, hurry, stay, need, lost, ever, pull, year, keep, hurt, ever, clean, sleep, need, well, sit, most, hurry, stay, sleep, stay, another, year, also, clean, most, well, hurt, sit

End — Police

Have students cut out the game board and cars. They paste the game board on construction paper. Players roll a die and move the number of spaces shown. They read the word they land on. If they say the word incorrectly, they lose their next turn. The first player to the police station wins.

Games for Stories 13-16
Building Sight Vocabulary 3, SV 6212-1

Name _____ Date _____

1. Did you _____ your hand?
   hurt   well

2. Keep your hurt hand _____.
                      most   clean

3. _____ of us are well.
   Most   Keep

4. Can most of us _____ here?
                  sit   well

5. I will _____ clean today.
         hurt   keep

6. Can I have _____ wish?
             year   another

7. I am _____ and need help.
       pull   lost

8. We _____ lost our way.
     hurry   also

9. _____ your hand away.
   Pull   Ever

10. Did you _____ pull so hard?
           ever   year

Have students trace the sentence and pick the missing word to complete the sentence. Have them write the missing word on the line.

Review of Stories 13-16
Building Sight Vocabulary 3, SV 6212-1

Name _____ Date _____

Shall we keep it or use it?

As they left, they gave their money .

shall   left   or   gave

■   s h e l e f t i t o u t t h e r e

_____

_ _

_____

➡ give   told   give   gave

leave   gave   _____   _____

run   left   _____   _____

tell   thought   _____   _____

think   ran   _____   _____

▲   1. Mandy gave it to me when she _____.

2. Shall we go or _____ we stay?

3. I _____ him a ride.

4. I shall not eat _____ sleep.

● Have students read the Key Sentences, read the words below, and draw a line from each word to the same word in the Key Sentences. ■ Each student should run a finger under the letters until a word is found. Have them put a mark between the words. They should then write the sentence on the line leaving a space between each word and using capitalization and punctuation. ➡ Have students draw lines to match the two forms of the verb and then write the verbs on the lines. ▲ Have students read each sentence and write one of the new words in the blank.

Lesson 17: Practice
Building Sight Vocabulary 3, SV 6212-1

Name _____   Date _____

■

| We / They | left / gave | it to the birds 🍂 / something good |

_____

- -

_____

➡ pull + s   = _____

pull + ed   = _____

pull + ing   = _____

▲ left + over   = _____

up + set   = _____

★   I. I lost   what was left.

2. Kim left her books 📚   here, also.

3. Why did you   one this year.

4. He gave Nat   go this year?

● Have students read each word aloud and trace it. ■ Have students choose a phrase from each box and then write the sentence on the line. ➡ Have students write the -s, -ed, and -ing forms of the word. ▲ Have students combine the two words to form compound words. ★ Have students read the sentence stem at the left and the possible endings at the right. Have them choose the ending that makes sense and draw a line to connect the two sentence parts.

Lesson 17: Practice

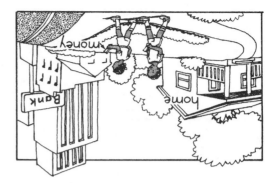

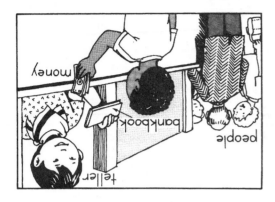

Page 1

Story 17
The Bank Teller

Nat and Kim did some work for their dad. He gave them some money when they were done.

Kim said, "What shall we do, Nat? Shall we keep it or use it?"

Nat said, "Let's keep our money for another time. Shall we keep all of it, or just most of it?"

Name _____

Page 2

"It would not hurt if we left part of our money at home. We should keep most of our money at the bank," said Kim.

"We could get something for Mom and Dad with some of it," said Nat.

Nat and Kim took most of their money to the bank. They left part of their money at home.

Page 3

Nat pulled out his money and gave it to the teller. Kim gave her money to the teller, also. The teller gave each of them a bankbook.

She said, "This will tell you how much money you have left here. Many people have left their money here. It is a good place to keep it."

Page 4

"You can leave your money for a long time or take it out soon," said the teller. "We shall look after your money for you."

As Kim left she said, "The bank is a good place for our money. It will not get lost. We shall always keep our money in the bank."

As they left, they were happy they gave their money.

Name _____   Date _____

Yes, I want to buy it myself if it does not cost much.

●   buy   myself   yes   cost

■   h o w m u c h d o e s t h i s c o s t

_____

– –

_____

➡ grow   lost   start   would

cost   know   should   day

hot   told   stay   tell

cold   not   well   part

▲ walk   walker   help   _____

buy   _____   new   _____

★   1. What shall I _____ for myself?

     2. _____, it costs too much to buy.

     3. Tony told me the _____.

     4. I think I shall sleep by _____.

● Have students read the Key Sentence, read the words below, and draw a line from each word to the same word in the Key Sentence. ■ Each student should run a finger under the letters until a word is found. Have them put a mark between the words. They should then write the sentence on the line leaving a space between each word and using capitalization and punctuation. ➡ Have students draw lines to match the rhyming words. ▲ Have students write the *-er* form of the words. ★ Have students read each sentence and write one of the new words in the blank.

Lesson 18: Practice

Building Sight Vocabulary 3, SV 6212-1

Name _____ Date _____

---

buy   myself   yes   cost

gave   left   or   shall

■

| I shall | buy it for | myself |
| Do I need to | keep it for | Dan |

_____

- -

_____

➡ buy + s   =   _____

buy + er   =   _____

buy + ing   =   _____

▲ hurried┄┄   try   ▲ tried   hurry
                      ▲
carries ┄┄┄➤ hurry   ▲ hurries   carry
                      ▲
tries   carry   ▲ carried   try
                      ▲

★ 1. What shall I   buy myself?

2. He left before   find out the cost.

3. We hurried   he gave me any.

4. Yes, I shall   to buy another one.

● Have students read each word aloud and trace it. ■ Have students choose a phrase from each box and then write the sentence on the line. ➡ Have students write the -s, -er, and -ing forms of the word. ▲ Have students draw lines to match each verb with its base word. ★ Have students read the sentence stem at the left and the possible endings at the right. Have them choose the ending that makes sense and draw a line to connect the two sentence parts.

Story 18
The Department Store

"I would like to buy something. May I go in the department store with you?" Jenny asked her dad.

"Yes, you may go. A department store has many kinds of goods you can buy," said Dad. "Some things cost only a little. Other goods cost much more."

Name _____

"I have enough to buy that game for myself. May I?" Jenny asked.

"Yes. You may buy what you want with your own money," Dad said.

Jenny took her money to the clerk.

"Thank you," he said.

"I like to buy things by myself," Jenny said as they left.

4

Jenny saw a game she wanted.

"Do you want to buy the game?" Dad asked.

"Yes, I want to buy it myself if it does not cost much," said Jenny. "I need to find out how much it costs."

"Come back after you find out," Dad told her.

2

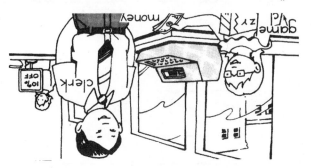

"Have you found something you wish to buy?" the clerk asked.

"Yes. Does this game cost very much? Do I have enough money to buy it for myself?" asked Jenny.

"Yes, you do," said the clerk. "Do you like to play this game better than that one?"

"Yes, this one is better! It is fun!" said Jenny.

3

After I <u>ate</u> a <u>few</u>, I was <u>full</u>.   I liked my <u>drink</u> best.

●   ate   few   full   drink

■   L a n a t e a f e w g r a p e s

_____

- -

_____

➡ try   tr<u>ies</u>   trie<u>d</u>

    hurry   _____   _____

    carry   _____   _____

▲ ate   shall   1. _____   4. _____

    few   or   2. _____   5. _____

    drink   yes   3. _____   6. _____

★ 1. Eric tries to _____ milk 🥛 every day.

    2. Are you too _____ to drink this?

    3. Tony _____ two apples 🍎.

    4. Now he will eat a _____ more.

● Have students read the Key Sentences, read the words below, and draw a line from each word to the same word in the Key Sentences. ■ Each student should run a finger under the letters until a word is found. Have them put a mark between the words. They should then write the sentence on the line leaving a space between each word and using capitalization and punctuation. ➡ Have students write the *-es* and *-ed* forms of the words. ▲ Have students write the words in alphabetical order. ★ Have students read each sentence and write one of the new words in the blank.

Lesson 19: Practice
Building Sight Vocabulary 3, SV 6212-1

●   ate   few   full   drink

      buy   yes   cost   myself

■

Joy Ed	likes gave Dan	a few things to eat something to drink

_____

- -

_____

➡ clean + s   = _____

   clean + ing   = _____

   clean + er   = _____

▲ st<u>ay</u>   lost   full   think

   few   aw<u>ay</u>   drink   away

   cost   new   stay   pull

★   l. I want to   to buy most of it.

   2. Yes, I ate   very much?

   3. Does it cost   buy a few pencils .

   4. I need   a few of them.

● Have students read each word aloud and trace it. ■ Have students choose a phrase from each box and then write the sentence on the line. ➡ Have students write the -s, -ing, and -er forms of the word. ▲ Have students draw lines to match the rhyming words. ★ Have students read the sentence stem at the left and the possible endings at the right. Have them choose the ending that makes sense and draw a line to connect the two sentence parts.

There were just a few small things left.

Kim ate most of hers, too.

Nat ate all of his food.

to eat and drink.

carrying good things

was back

the waiter

Soon

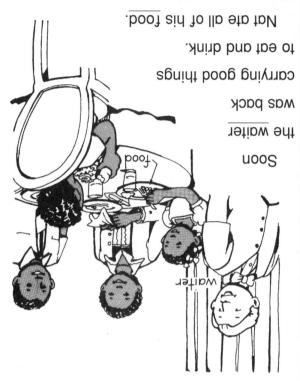

few more people today."

people who come in. We will have only a

this table. Then it will be ready for the next

She said, "After you leave, I will clean off

kind of work she did.

set their table. Kim asked her what other

While the waiter was away, the attendant

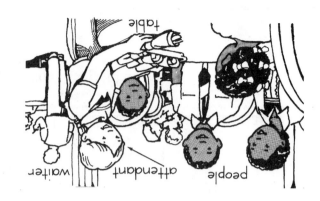

"You ate well," said Mom. "You must like the food here."

"Yes. I liked everything!" said Nat. "I have never been so full!"

"I liked what I ate. After I ate a few, I was full. I liked my drink best," said Kim.

"I am full, too," said Dad. "This restaurant has good things to eat and drink. We will have to come back again soon."

Story 19
The Restaurant

Kim and Nat liked to go to Red's Restaurant. Many people ate there. The restaurant was very full.

The waiter gave them each a menu. The menu told of many good things to eat and drink. There were a few things Nat and Kim liked best. Mom helped them each pick out good things to eat.

Name _____

Name _____   Date _____

Please tell Mr. Rider I am not through yet.

●   Mr.   through   yet   please

■   m r . w h i t e i s t h r o u g h n o w

_____

_ _

_____

➡   live   lived   living

place   _____   _____

please   _____   _____

use   _____   _____

▲ has + not = hasn't   was + not = _____

do + not = _____   did + not = _____

★   I. May I _____ have a few grapes 🍇 ?

2. Tony was pleased when he got _____.

3. Can you find _____ Walker, please?

4. It is not time to go _____.

● Have students read the Key Sentence, read the words below, and draw a line from each word to the same word in the Key Sentence. ■ Each student should run a finger under the letters until a word is found. Have them put a mark between the words. They should then write the sentence on the line leaving a space between each word and using capitalization and punctuation. ➡ Have students write the -ed and -ing forms of the words. ▲ Have students combine the two words to form contractions. ★ Have students read each sentence and write one of the new words in the blank.

© Steck-Vaughn Company   73   **Lesson 20: Practice**   Building Sight Vocabulary 3, SV 6212-1

Name _____   Date _____

Mr.   through   yet   please
ate   full   few   drink

■
| Mr. Brown | ate when he | was ready |
| Mr. White | ran when he | got through |

_____

- -

_____

➡ a y x x t h r o u g h x x f
t e x p l e a s e f u l l e
e t x d r i n k M r . x x w

▲ do + not = _____   can + not = _____

are + not = _____   did + not = _____

is + not   = _____   have + not = _____

★ 1. Please drink   here yet?

2. Run through   the door 🚪 together.

3. I am not   all of it.

4. Why isn't Mr. Black   through yet.

● Have students read each word aloud and trace it. ■ Have students choose a phrase from each box and then write the sentence on the line. ➡ Have students find and circle the words from the ● activity in the puzzle. ▲ Have students combine the two words to form contractions. ★ Have students read the sentence stem at the left and the possible endings at the right. Have them choose the ending that makes sense and draw a line to connect the two sentence parts.

Lesson 20: Practice
Building Sight Vocabulary 3, SV 6212-1

The <u>mechanic</u> worked on Nat's <u>car</u>. He worked for a long time.

Nat's dad called Mr. Walker and said, "Are you through with my <u>car</u> yet?"

Mr. Walker asked the <u>mechanic</u> about Nat's <u>car</u>. The <u>mechanic</u> said, "Please tell Mr. Rider I am not through yet. He should call back around five."

Dad was very pleased to find that Mr. Walker was at the gas station.

Nat said, "Please help us. The <u>car</u> is about to stop. Is your <u>mechanic</u> here yet?"

"Yes, he is. But he can not work on it yet," said Mr. Walker. "He will work on it as soon as he is through with another <u>car</u>. Please leave your <u>car</u> over there."

The <u>mechanic</u> worked on the <u>car</u> some more. He hurried so that he would be through by five.

When he was through, he took the <u>car</u> out to see how it would run. The <u>mechanic</u> told Mr. Walker what he had done to the <u>car</u>.

Mr Walker said, "You did good, fast work. Nat's dad will be pleased to see how well his <u>car</u> is running."

Story 20
The Mechanic

Nat and his dad were riding in the <u>car</u>. All at once the <u>car</u> was not running right.

"Let's hurry to Mr. Walker's <u>gas station</u>," said Dad. "It is only a little way from here. Once we get there, they will know what needs to be done."

They hurried to the <u>gas station</u>.

Name_____

Name _____   Date _____

PRODUCE			MEAT		

ate	yet	few	left	or	gave
Mr.	drink	full	please	buy	myself
through	few	yet	shall	yes	cost

Have students paste the page on construction paper and cut out the game board and word cards. Playing in pairs, students combine their word cards and turn them face down in a pile. Students take turns drawing a card and reading it. If they read the word correctly, they place it on the board in the appropriate food section. If read incorrectly, the student returns it to the bottom of the card pile. The first student to place each food in the correct classification wins.

Game for Stories 17-20
Building Sight Vocabulary 3, SV 6212-1

Name _____   Date _____

1. I _____ you what was left.
   gave   yes

2. How much does it _____?
   cost   buy

3. I will _____ one or two.
   left   buy

4. Shall I go right _____ left?
   or   of

5. Hold out your _____ hand.
   shall   left

6. We ate and got _____.
   few   full

7. Are you _____ eating yet?
   please   through

8. A _____ of us are through.
   full   few

9. Please have a cold _____.
   drink   full

10. Is _____ Black here yet?
    Mr.   few

Have students trace the sentence and pick the missing word to complete the sentence. Have them write the missing word on the line.

© Steck-Vaughn Company

Review of Stories 17-20
Building Sight Vocabulary 3, SV 6212-1

● What is the <u>funny</u> <u>round</u> thing?

They could <u>fall</u> from that <u>high</u> up.

funny   round   fall   high

■   h o w h i g h c a n i t g o

_____

- -

_____

➡ he + i̸s   he's

she + i̸s   _____

it + i̸s   _____

he + i̸s   _____

there + i̸s   _____

where + i̸s   _____

▲ com̸e   com<u>ing</u>

give   _____

live   _____

ride   _____

come   _____

have   _____

★ 1. The funny clown 🤡 went up _____.

2. A wheel ⊛ is _____.

3. The leaves 🍂 will _____ on us.

4. She's so _____ she makes me laugh.

● Have students read the Key Sentences, read the words below, and draw a line from each word to the same word in the Key Sentences. ■ Each student should run a finger under the letters until a word is found. Have them put a mark between the words. They should then write the sentence on the line leaving a space between each word and using capitalization and punctuation. ➡ Have students combine the two words to form contractions. ▲ Have students cross out the e in each word and write the -ing form of the word. ★ Have students read each sentence and write one of the new words in the blank.

Lesson 21: Practice
Building Sight Vocabulary 3, SV 6212-1

funny   round   fall   yet

Mr.   through   yet   please

A round ball ◯	can fall	on you
A funny leaf 🍂	came down	from up high

_____

_ _

_____

➡ hard + er = _____

full + er   = _____

wish + er = _____

▲ hurry _____   hurried _____

hurries _____   hurrying _____

★ 1. Please don't run   if you are up high.

2. Eric hurried to get   because you could fall.

3. Please stop that   the round ball ◯.

4. You can fall   funny singing.

● Have students read each word aloud and trace it. ■ Have students choose a phrase from each box and then write the sentence on the line. ➡ Have students write the *-er* form of the words. ▲ Show students how the word *hurry* changes with each ending. Have students write the *-es, -ed,* and *-ing* forms of the word. ★ Have students read the sentence stem at the left and the possible endings at the right. Have them choose the ending that makes sense and draw a line to connect the two sentence parts.

Lesson 21: Practice

Building Sight Vocabulary 3, SV 6212-1

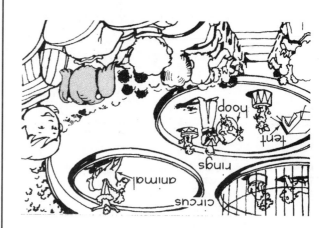

Story 21
The Circus Performers

Mandy and Dan were saying and doing funny things. They would fall down and laugh.

Soon Mandy saw a truck go by. It had a round sign on it which said, "Circus Today."

"Let's go to the circus. It only comes for seven days each fall," said Mandy.

Name _____

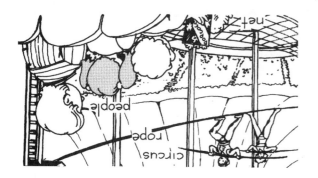

Mom took Mandy and Dan to the circus. They went in a big, round tent and looked for a place to sit up high. They wanted to see all three big round rings.

They saw many animals doing funny things. Some animals were jumping through big, round hoops.

Some people were walking on a rope way up high.

"Oh, oh!" said Dan. "They could fall from that high up."

A net would stop them. But, they did not fall.

Mandy and Dan liked the circus. They ate popcorn and had something good to drink.

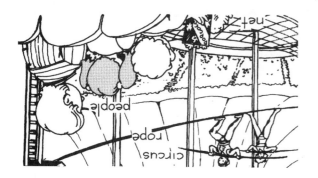

The clowns had on funny things. They did funny things, too. One had a big, round hoop that she would fall through. Then the others would fall down and laugh.

"What is the funny round thing?" said Mandy.

"It is a hoop," said Mom.

Dan said, "This was fun! I like the clowns the best. I want to come next year!"

4

Name _____ Date _____

He was <u>fine</u> <u>until</u> today. | Mandy <u>made</u> him <u>warm</u>.

fine   until   made   warm

■   t o d a y i s t o o w a r m

_____
— — — — — — — — — — — — — — — — — — — —
_____

➡ some + one   = _____

some + place = _____

some + time   = _____

some + where = _____

some + thing = _____

▲ 1. It is too _____ under this blanket .

2. The light in here is just _____.

3. Someone _____ a big kite .

4. Leave the light on _____ you go.

● Have students read the Key Sentences, read the words below, and draw a line from each word to the same word in the Key Sentences. ■ Each student should run a finger under the letters until a word is found. Have them put a mark between the words. They should then write the sentence on the line leaving a space between each word and using capitalization and punctuation. ➡ Have students combine the two words to form compound words. ▲ Have students read each sentence and write one of the new words in the blank.

© Steck-Vaughn Company

Lesson 22: Practice
Building Sight Vocabulary 3, SV 6212-1

Name _____   Date _____

warm   until   fine   made

round   high   funny   fall

■

| It is too warm | to run | and sing |
| The day is fine | to play | around |

_____

- -

_____

➡ carry + ed = <u>carried</u>

hurry + ed = _____

try + ed   = _____

▲   f f r o u n d r m h i g h g h

x m a d e f i n e f u n n y x

e u n t i l w a r m l f a l l

★   1. Something funny   sit up high.

2. I tried to   he made me fall.

3. It is too warm   to sleep.

4. I was fine until   makes me laugh.

● Have students read each word aloud and trace it. ■ Have students choose a phrase from each box and then write the
sentence on the line. ➡ Have students write the -ed form of the words. ▲ Have students find and circle the words from
the ● activity in the puzzle. ★ Have students read the sentence stem at the left and the possible endings at the right.
Have them choose the ending that makes sense and draw a line to connect the two sentence parts.

Lesson 22: Practice
Building Sight Vocabulary 3, SV 6212-1

"Has Tip ever been here?" asked Dr. Day.

"Yes. You made him well before," said Mandy.

He made Tip sit on a table.

"Tip is a little warmer than he should be," said Dr. Day.

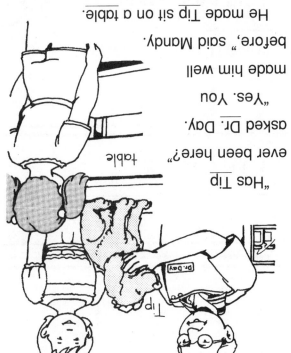

"Mom, we need to take Tip to the vet. He was fine until today. He was warm. Now he is too cold!" said Mandy.

"Stay here with him until I am ready to go," said Mom. "Try to keep him warm."

"I will hold him until the vet sees him. The vet is a fine doctor. He made Tip well once before," said Mandy.

Mandy made him warm.

When Dr. Day was through looking at Tip, he said, "Give Tip enough to eat and drink. Let him sleep all he can. Keep him in until it is warm enough to go out to play. He must not get too cold. Make him take this every day for six days. Tip will be fine soon."

"Thank you. You are a fine vet," said Mandy.

Story 22
The Veterinarian

Mandy could not find Tip. She looked all over. She did not find him until she looked under the bed.

"You do not look so fine," she said. Tip did funny things when Mandy tried to hold him. It made her think he must hurt someplace.

"He is much too warm," she said.

Name _____

Name _____   Date _____

"It is such a big place," said Mrs. Weller.

Everyone can see the same from far away.

●   same   such   far   Mrs.

■   t h i s i s s u c h a f i n e d o g

_____

- -

_____

➡ well   ➡ bring   ➡ small

t __ __ __   s __ __ __   f __ __ __

s __ __ __   w __ __ __   c __ __ __

__ __ __ __   __ __ __ __   __ __ __ __

▲   1. This is _____ a good drink, Mrs. Green.

2. Is your mom _____ Brown?

3. The cat 🐱 ran _____ away.

4. Do you think you lost it in the _____ place?

● Have students read the Key Sentences, read the words below, and draw a line from each word to the same word in the Key Sentences. ■ Each student should run a finger under the letters until a word is found. Have them put a mark between the words. They should then write the sentence on the line leaving a space between each word and using capitalization and punctuation. ➡ Have students form rhyming words for each word family. ▲ Have students read each sentence and write one of the new words in the blank.

Lesson 23: Practice
Building Sight Vocabulary 3, SV 6212-1

Name _____   Date _____

same   such   far   Mrs.

warm   until   fine   made

| Mrs. Green
Mrs. Brown | will sit
will sleep | in the same place
until I call her |

_____

- -

_____

➡ warm + er = _____

high + er = _____

▲

s a m e M m a d e f t l s
t l s e M r s . f i a e u
u n t i l c f a a n a a c
t w a r m w m s r e w m h

★ 1. I ate until   a pretty day.

2. Mrs. Day lives   to get that far?

3. I thought it was such   far away.

4. How long will it take   I was full.

● Have students read each word aloud and trace it. ■ Have students choose a phrase from each box and then write the sentence on the line. ➡ Have students write the *-er* form of the words. ▲ Have students find and circle the words from the ● activity in the puzzle. ★ Have students read the sentence stem at the left and the possible endings at the right. Have them choose the ending that makes sense and draw a line to connect the two sentence parts.

© Steck-Vaughn Company

Lesson 23: Practice
Building Sight Vocabulary 3, SV 6212-1

"We do the play on this stage. It is such a big place," said Mrs. Weller. "Everyone can see the same from far away." Soon the actors went on stage.

"This is the same play you saw before, Tony," said Mrs. Weller. "We do the same play many times. We try to do it the same every time."

"Oh, yes!" they all said at the same time.

"Thank you," said Mrs. Weller. "Would you like to see the theater?"

"Tony says you are such a good actor," said Jenny.

"This is my grandma, Mrs. Weller," he said.

Tony was in such a hurry to see his grandma that he ran to find her.

The children went to sit not far from the stage. Someone put the lights off and on many times until everyone was ready. Soon the play started.

When it was over, Jenny said, "Oh, Mrs. Weller! It was such a good play. You are such a fine actor. I wish I could see every play that you do!"

Story 23
The Actor

"I am going to see my grandma," said Tony. "She lives far away, but she is an actor in a play that is at our theater. Do you want to go with me to see her?"

"Yes, we do. I didn't know someone could be a grandma and an actor at the same time," said Eric.

Name _____

●

She would <u>name</u> all the <u>old</u> things there.

I <u>love</u> the <u>end</u> the best.

love   old   end   name

■   w h a t i s y o u r n a m e , p l e a s e

_____

– –

_____

➡ name   name<u>s</u>   nam<u>ed</u>

love   _____   _____

live   _____   _____

like   _____   _____

name   _____   _____

▲ 1. Today I am ten years _____.

2. At the _____ of the year I will be six.

3. I _____ my new yellow cat .

4. What is your first _____?

● Have students read the Key Sentences, read the words below, and draw a line from each word to the same word in the Key Sentences. ■ Each student should run a finger under the letters until a word is found. Have them put a mark between the words. They should then write the sentence on the line leaving a space between each word and using capitalization and punctuation. ➡ Have students write the -s and -ed forms of the words. ▲ Have students read each sentence and write one of the new words in the blank.

Name _____ Date _____

● name   old   end   love

Mrs.   far   such   same

■ | I love
I have | to sleep
to end my day | in the same place
here |

_____

– –

_____

➡ ending + s   =   _____

building + s   =   _____

▲   n l s s u c h f a r
     a o a l e n d v e m
     m v m v n o l d M r
     e e e w l d M r s .

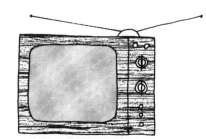

★ 1. The end of the road   my name?

   2. Do you know   is not very far.

   3. The big buildings   us the old book 📖.

   4. Mrs. Black will read   look the same.

● Have students read each word aloud and trace it. ■ Have students choose a phrase from each box and then write the sentence on the line. ➡ Have students write the -s form of the words. ▲ Have students find and circle the words from the ● activity in the puzzle. ★ Have students read the sentence stem at the left and the possible endings at the right. Have them choose the ending that makes sense and draw a line to connect the two sentence parts.

88

each kind of dinosaur.
old. Eric always asked Mrs. Fuller to name
lived for a long time. The bones were very
bones were there. The dinosaurs have not
the far end of the building. The dinosaur
The place that Eric liked the best was at

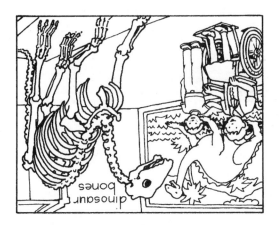

Fuller.
"Many people love that one," said Mrs.
Fall.' "
Orange
"I know the name of it. It is called 'Orange
"I love the one of the big tree," said Eric.
Fuller.
Here we have very old paintings," said Mrs.
at the museum. I love the end the best.
"I like to show people the things we have

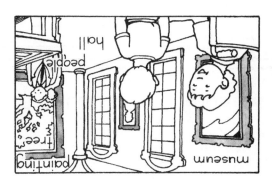

Sometimes Eric and Mrs. Fuller would sit

at the end of a long <u>hall</u> of the museum. She

would name all the old things there. Soon he

could name all the things, too.

Eric loved to go to the <u>museum</u>. He

thought that sometime he would like to work

there.

Story 24
The Museum Curator

Eric loves to go to the old <u>museum</u>. It is at

the end of the <u>street</u>. At the end of a day at

<u>school</u>, he likes to walk to the old <u>museum</u>.

He likes to see the <u>curator</u>. Her name is Mrs.

Fuller. She always tells Eric the names of the

things in the <u>museum</u>. She tells him about new

things and about old things.

Name _____

The last number called was ours.

We are going to fly along, too.

●   last   number   along   fly

■   t h e l a s t n u m b e r i s e i g h t

_____

- -

_____

➡ carry   carries   carrying

hurry   _____   _____

fly   _____   _____

try   _____   _____

carry   _____   _____

▲   1. Come _____ and fly with us.

2. The last _____ I will call is ten.

3. Last year I got to _____ in a plane  .

4. Hurry, so you will not be _____ .

● Have students read the Key Sentences, read the words below, and draw a line from each word to the same word in the Key Sentences. ■ Each student should run a finger under the letters until a word is found. Have them put a mark between the words. They should then write the sentence on the line leaving a space between each word and using capitalization and punctuation. ➡ Have students write the -es and -ing forms of the words. ▲ Have students read each sentence and write one of the new words in the blank.

fly   along   number   last

love   end   old   name

The last one The old plane ✈	went will fly	after them up high

_____

_ _

➡ did + not   =   _____

would + not   =   _____

have + not   =   _____

▲
```
h n u m b e r a
t c k a l o n g
```
```
f a x l o v e o e
l x n a m e x l n l d
y x x l a s t d d x x
```

★ 1. See the birds 🕊   name at the end.

2. Put your   fly along together.

3. I love to see   the birds 🕊 fly.

4. At last I am   nine years old.

● Have students read each word aloud and trace it. ■ Have students choose a phrase from each box and then write the sentence on the line. ➡ Have students combine the two words to form contractions. ▲ Have students find and circle the words from the ● activity in the puzzle. ★ Have students read the sentence stem at the left and the possible endings at the right. Have them choose the ending that makes sense and draw a line to connect the two sentence parts.

pilot

Just then the pilot walked over.

"We are going to fly along, too," Nat said to the pilot.

"What is your name?" he asked.

Nat said, "My name is Nat and this is Kim. We are flying to a place far away."

"We will be taking off soon," said the pilot. "We are happy to have you along with us."

"Where are you going?" the flight attendant asked.

"We are going far away. We have to fly to get there," said Kim.

"Have you ever been on a plane before?" asked the flight attendant.

"Yes, I love to fly," said Nat. "Kim didn't come along last year. But she is going this year."

plane
flight attendant

plane
flight attendant

Nat and Kim hurried along to sit down. The flight attendant said he would bring them something good to eat and drink after the plane was flying high.

Nat and Kim were both happy to be on their way at last.

4

Story 25
The Airplane

Kim and Nat were walking along with their dad in the airport. Some numbers were called out.

"Did they call our flight number?" asked Kim.

"The last number called was ours," said Dad.

Nat and Kim were not the last ones to get on the plane. A number of other people ran to the plane.

Gate 2 airport
plane
people
Flight number 7
Chicago 2:00

Name _____

Name _____   Date _____

PASTE	STOP
Mrs. White made	until we left
big and round	made it through
fall down	keep it the same
up too high	love old things
a fine place	stay up high
last number called	do not fall
name at the end	not very funny
come fly along	such a warm day
START	PASTE

Have students cut out and paste together the tightrope. They take turns reading the phrases in order from start to finish. If a student misses a word, he or she goes back to START and begins again on the next turn. The first student to make it to STOP with no errors is the winner.

1. Did you _____ and get hurt?
   fall   warm

2. I was warm _____ just now.
   fine   until

3. Your talk was very _____.
   made   funny

4. Dan make a _____ wish.
   fine   until

5. I have _____ a long name.
   end   such

6. How _____ is Mrs. Green?
   old   name

7. I can run as _____ as you.
   far   love

8. I _____ this time of year.
   such   love

9. I knew you would go _____.
   number   along

10. I am the _____ one to go.
    last   name

Have students trace the sentence and pick the missing word to complete the sentence. Have them write the missing word on the line.

ANSWER KEY

Page 4 1. every 2. place 3. goes 4. own 5. thought 6. build 7. part 8. each 9. which 10. other 11. than 12. more 13. next 14. sure 15. kind 16. should 17. pick 18. start 19. grow 20. enough 21. set 22. small 23. carry 24. cold

Page 5 1. along 2. fly 3. last 4. number 5. old 6. cost 7. need 8. bring 9. grow 10. made 11. another 12. please 13. sleep 14. hold 15. through 16. cost 17. sit 18. yes 19. please 20. other 21. end 22. which 23. warm 24. buy

Page 11 1. an 2. took 3. while 4. after

Page 12 while, hand/back/took, an , after 1. She's going over to him. 2. What do you think comes after three? 3. It is fun to laugh together. 4. What will we do after a while?

Page 14 1. best 2. sing 3. does 4. hold

Page 15 hold, sing, best/took, does 1. Can you hold the ball for a while? 2. It took a long time. 3. He will sing after I try to sing my best. 4. She always does her very best.

Page 17 1. wish 2. ready 3. ready/done 4. bring

Page 18 ready, wish, bring 1. I am singing my very best for you. 2. He always brings the pink ball. 3. I wish I could go, too. 4. Are you ready to make a wish?

Page 21 1. hold 2. best 3. sing 4. two 5. ready 6. hold 7. one 8. done 9. after 10. eight

Page 22 1. read 2. once 3. nothing 4. told

Page 23 told, read/wish, nothing 1. Bring it when it is done. 2. Once I had a big blue kite. 3. He told me to make a wish. 4. I have nothing to read.

Page 25 1. both 2. hard 3. only 4. Thank

Page 26 1. hard, both/told, thank, only 1. Have you read that long book? 2. Both of you can read this. 3. I am only trying to thank you.

Page 28 1. after 2. bring 3. done 4. every 1. Every 2. place 3. goes 4. thought 5. own

Page 29 1. Everyone goes to my place to eat. 2. I thought you had your own. 3. I thought it was over here. 4. Everything goes together.

Page 31 1. other 2. Which 3. part 4. each 5. build

Page 32 1. The other part goes with this. 2. Is anyone living in that new place? 3. I thought he had his own place. 4. Which part will you build?

Page 35 1. goes 2. every 3. build 4. own 5. each 6. told 7. only 8. hard 9. nothing 10. once

Page 36 1. more 2. than 3. next 4. sure

Page 37 1. He is sure to do it next time. 2. Which one has more green in it? 3. I can jump more times than you can. 4. Which part will you sing next?

Page 39 1. kind 2. should 3. start 4. Pick

Page 40 1. We couldn't start over again. 2. Say kind things to your cat. 3. Did Mandy pick more than Lan? 4. What should I say to them?

Page 42 1. small 2. enough 3. grow 4. set

Page 43 1. This cat is kind of small. 2. Will it grow big enough? 3. It should grow if it eats enough. 4. Can you pick three small apples?

Page 45 1. cold 2. does 3. each 4. first 5. grow 6. hot 1. leave 2. hot 3. carry/ leave 4. cold

Page 46 1. I will leave because it is too hot. 2. Can you carry a small basket? 3. Set it down in these brown leaves. 4. The small one will grow big.

Page 49 1. than 2. kind 3. more 4. next 5. pick 6. enough 7. carry 8. cold 9. grow 10. set

Page 50 1. Sit/Stay 2. sleep 3. sit 4. hurt

Page 51 1. We will leave in the daytime. 2. The leaves will not stay green. 3. Did the four of them leave? 4. I never sit where it is hot.

Page 53 1. well 2. most 3. clean 4. Keep

Page 54 1. Most of them grow well here. 2. It will not hurt to stay clean. 3. I have had enough sleep. 4. You must keep most of the red ones.

Page 56 1. need 2. another 3. hurry 4. ever

Page 57 1. I will keep nine red balloons. 2. This is cleaner than the blue one. 3. You need to stay all day. 4. Have you ever had a smaller car?

Page 59 1. Pull 2. also 3. lost 4. year

Page 60 1. I lost another one this year. 2. I don't know where I lost it. 3. Do you ever need help? 4. She also got her wish.

Building Sight Vocabulary 3, SV 6212-1

ANSWER KEY

Page 63 1. hurt 2. clean 3. Most 4. sit 5. keep 6. another 7. lost 8. also 9. Pull 10. ever

Page 64 1. left 2. shall 3. gave 4. or

Page 65 1. I lost one this year. or I lost what was left.
2. Kim left her books here, also.
3. Why did you go this year?
4. He gave Nat what was left. or He gave Nat one this year.

Page 67 1. buy 2. Yes 3. cost 4. myself

Page 68 1. What shall I buy myself? 2. He left before he gave me any. 3. We hurried to buy another one. 4. Yes, I shall find out the cost.

Page 70 1. ate 2. drink 3. few 4. or 5. shall 6. yes 1. drink 2. full 3. ate 4. few

Page 71 1. I want to buy a few pencils. 2. Yes, I ate a few of them. 3. Does it cost very much? 4. I need to buy most of it.

Page 73 1. please 2. through 3. Mr. 4. yet

Page 74 1. Please drink all of it. 2. Run through the door together. 3. I am not through yet. 4. Why isn't Mr. Black here yet?

Page 77 1. gave 2. cost 3. buy 4. or 5. left 6. full 7. through 8. few 9. drink 10. Mr.

Page 78 1. high 2. round 3. fall 4. funny

Page 79 1. Please don't run because you could fall. 2. Eric hurried to get the round ball. 3. Please stop that funny singing. 4. You can fall if you are up high.

Page 81 1. warm 2. fine 3. made 4. until

Page 82 1. Something funny makes me laugh. 2. I tried to sit up high. 3. It is too warm to sleep. 4. I was fine until he made me fall.

Page 84 1. such 2. Mrs. 3. far 4. same

Page 85 1. I ate until I was full. 2. Mrs. Day lives far away. 3. I thought it was such a pretty day. 4. How long will it take to get that far?

Page 87 1. old 2. end 3. love 4. name

Page 88 1. The end of the road is not very far. 2. Do you know my name? 3. The big buildings look the same. 4. Mrs. Black will read us the old book.

Page 90 1. along 2. number 3. fly 4. last

Page 91 1. See the birds fly along together. 2. Put your name at the end. 3. I love to see the birds fly. 4. At last I am nine years old.

Page 94 1. fall 2. until 3. funny 4. fine 5. such 6. old 7. far 8. love 9. along 10. last

Building Sight Vocabulary 3, SV 6212-1